# Up, Up and Away

## *NOTTINGHAMSHIRE*

Edited by Sarah Andrew

First published in Great Britain in 2000 by
*YOUNG WRITERS*
Remus House,
Coltsfoot Drive,
Peterborough, PE2 9JX
Telephone  (01733) 890066

HB ISBN 0 75432 300 5
SB ISBN 0 75432 301 3

# FOREWORD

This year, the Young Writers' Up, Up & Away competition proudly presents a showcase of the best poetic talent from over 70,000 up-and-coming writers nationwide.

Successful in continuing our aim of promoting writing and creativity in children, our regional anthologies give a vivid insight into the thoughts, emotions and experiences of today's younger generation, displaying their inventive writing in its originality.

The thought, effort, imagination and hard work put into each poem impressed us all and again the task of editing proved challenging due to the quality of entries received, but was nevertheless enjoyable. We hope you are as pleased as we are with the final selection and that you continue to enjoy *Up, Up & Away Nottinghamshire* for many years to come.

# CONTENTS

Chetwynd Road Primary School

| | |
|---|---|
| Kayleigh Desnos | 80 |
| James Freeman | 80 |
| Alice Foster | 81 |
| Aiden Clarke | 81 |

**Highfields School**

| | |
|---|---|
| Hannah Senior | 82 |
| Matthew Willson | 82 |
| Lizzie Simmonds | 83 |
| Freddie Reid | 83 |
| Stephanie Derbyshire | 84 |

**Jesse Gray Primary School**

| | |
|---|---|
| Ciera Lovelock, Katerina McCourt, Colette Ayers & Tamsin Slade | 84 |
| Hanah Tindle | 85 |
| Hanisha Sethi | 86 |
| Fay Masters & Anna Thwaites | 86 |
| Ross Farrar | 87 |
| Laura-Jane Barker | 87 |
| Radhika Monisha Kalra | 88 |
| Katherine Stewart | 89 |
| Eleanor Barratt | 90 |
| Fred Brewin | 91 |
| Rebecca Wallis | 92 |
| James Marsh | 92 |
| Sarah Hudson | 93 |
| Beth Lacey | 94 |
| Heid Ford | 94 |
| Gracie Kildare | 94 |
| Hannah Percival | 95 |

**Keyworth Primary School**

| | |
|---|---|
| Lewis Williams | 95 |
| Sam Costall | 96 |
| Naomi Jameson | 96 |

| | |
|---|---:|
| Rebecca Blackburn | 97 |
| Symon Akinin | 97 |
| Samantha Collard | 98 |
| Grace Shields | 98 |
| Peter Frame | 98 |
| Tiffany Sisson | 99 |
| Amber Whittaker | 99 |
| Tara Elston | 100 |
| Michael Cox | 100 |
| Matthew Webster | 101 |
| Leah Fielding | 101 |
| Laura Blackburn | 102 |
| Stephanie Collard | 102 |
| Helen Cox | 103 |
| Sarah Blatherwick | 103 |
| Naomi Frame | 104 |
| Hollie Doughty | 104 |
| Aisha Kay Michael | 104 |

**King Edwin Primary School**

| | |
|---|---:|
| Grant Allen | 105 |
| Jacomo Nardi-Forster | 105 |
| Michaela Reeve | 106 |
| Nikki Thomas | 106 |
| Amber Lyons & Rebecca Rodgers | 106 |
| Caroline Foster | 107 |
| James Peacock | 107 |
| Hannah Peacock | 108 |
| Katie Holmes | 108 |
| Charlotte Saunders | 108 |
| Sarah Moore & Pia Jackson | 109 |
| Lucie Moore | 109 |
| Rachel Pearson | 110 |
| Jodie Thomas | 110 |
| Zack Whittaker | 111 |
| Charlotte Mendham & Alexandra J Peck | 111 |

*The Poems*

## THE UNUSUAL TEACHER

My teacher is very unusual
A black tie with a grey shirt
And a multicoloured suit
It's very unusual, don't you think?
And another thing
His shoes are like a ginger cat prowling on the loose
I hate them
It's not at all nice
Now for his hair!
His hair's alright ~ it's nearly white
His glasses are ever so jazzy
You see this is my teacher
The great Mr J
The greatest teacher of all.

**Hayley Channer (9)**
**Annesley Primary School**


## WAR

Planes flying
Planes bombing
People firing
People throwing
Grenades blowing
People dying
People crying
Planes crashing
Planes retreating
*That's war!*

**Jonathon Whysall (9)**
**Annesley Primary School**

## MY MUM

My mum's names is Jayne.
She's always a pain
She's always mean to me
As you can see.
She always says I'm wrong
When she knows I'm right
So saying she's wrong
Serves her right!

*Kelly-Jayne Meredith  (8)*
*Annesley Primary School*


## FISHING

Fishing in the sea.
Fishing in the sea.
What will we catch today?
Will it be big?
Will it be small?
But it doesn't matter at all.

*Lauren Johnson  (8)*
*Annesley Primary School*


## THE SUNSHINE

The sun is shining
The sky is blue
Butterflies flying
Birds singing
People laughing
Girls laughing

*Elizabeth Edwards  (8)*
*Annesley Primary School*

## WINTER

Winter snow
Fresh and beautiful
Plants are dying
Planes are flying
People wrapping
Fires warming
Winds blowing
Winter chilling

*Leona Huntley (8)*
*Annesley Primary School*


## CHRISTMAS DAY

Children smiling
Babies playing
Presents unwrapping
Parents laughing
Christmas going

*Lauren Massey (8)*
*Annesley Primary School*


## VALENTINE'S DAY

This is the best Valentine
He's so sweet, so handsome, so kind.
He always shows you how much he cares
He buys chocolates which we share
He has a really lovely name
And means everything to me
He is sweet, like a buttercup
Just like me.

*Leah Meakin (8)*
*Annesley Primary School*

## BABY GEORGIA

First you were in your mum's tummy
But now you are in the world
With big blue glistening eyes
And a smile which is just as nice
We waited for nine long months
And now you are here
With your slender long fingernails
Bushy eyebrows, black hair
But who cares what you look like
As long as you are alright.
          You are my cousin
*I love you.*

***Kelly Topham  (9)***
***Annesley Primary School***


## MY VALENTINE'S

People kissing
All day long
I want to sing
A happy song
Then all the people
Can sing along
Then Valentine's Day
Has really gone.

***Hannah Berrill  (9)***
***Annesley Primary School***

## SYCAMORE SEED

I am a seed
With the cool autumn wind
I am lifted from my home
I fall gently like a feather
floating from side to side
sometimes I am blown
in circles
turning upside down, and
spinning round and round
As I leave my home behind
and land on soft ground
and begin a new life
maybe I will be
the next millennium
tree

*Priyan Rayatt (8)*
*Attenborough Prep School*


## THINGS FALLING

Petal
A petal dropped off a flower
It fluttered and made zigzag lines
And scrambled to the ground.
As it fell to the ground
It made a rainbow colour.
The wind helped the petal
And safely fell to the ground.

*Kathryn Hales (9)*
*Attenborough Prep School*

## EGYPT

E   gypt is the gold sand.
G   old was Tutankhamun's treasure.
Y   oung was Tutankhamun when he was King.
P   ale was his face when Tutankhamun died.
T   utankhamun was a Pharaoh.

*Simon Worrall (8)*
*Attenborough Prep School*

## MY DIAMOND POEM

Jelly
Wobbly cold
Falling slipping tasty
Runny flavoured nice
Yummy pudding
Ice-cream

*Lucy Condon (8)*
*Attenborough Prep School*

## SPACE

Bright stars forever darkness until a falling star drops.
Just imagine going up there in a zooming rocket
Into outer space.
Seeing things nobody has seen before, planets and stars.
The whole Universe is ours.

*Madeleine Solloway (9)*
*Attenborough Prep School*

## MY MAGIC BOX

I will put into my box
a cold, dark, damp room,
a piece of a glittering moon
and a beautiful white horse.

I will put into my box
a diamond piece of lace,
a cone with the colours of the rainbow
and a hug from a friend.

I will put into my box
a baby's first giggle,
a diamond ring with silver
I will put in my box the world.

*Michael Webster  (9)*
*Attenborough Prep School*


## MY FAVOURITE BAND

S Club 7 are my favourite band
They dance about and wave their hands
Tina, Rachel, Hannah and Jo
They are the girls who have got the flow
Jon, Paul and Bradley are the boys in the band
They sing and dance around the land.
When they sing I think I am in heaven
And their new film is called Miami Seven.

*Thomas Reeder  (9)*
*Attenborough Prep School*

## THE MAGIC BOX

I will put in my box
The whole world, a yellow submarine,
a magnet the size of the world.

I will put in my box
A red devil, the rushing river,
The gushing winds, and a swirling waterfall.

I will put in my box
Gold coins with icicles hanging off them,
the centre of the sun and the magic moonlight.

*Matthew Howard  (9)*
*Attenborough Prep School*


## MY FAMILY

My annoying brother is such a pain,
Young, silly and violent he is.

Dad, Mum, Sam,
Auntie Tracy, Uncle Graham, Rachael, Millie,
Auntie Janice, Uncle Pete, Gavin, Liam

Flying around the house, my mum is tidying,
As bossy as can be as she goes
My dad comes home late every night because he gets stuck in traffic
I hate his untuneful singing, it gets on my nerves.
Living far away in Northampton are Grandma and Grandad.
Yuck! Feeling sick as you travel down to see them.

Grandma, Grandad, Uncle Mark, and Megan!

*Lauren Cox  (9)*
*Bramcote CE Primary School*

# CALM

Calm is the colour of blazing yellow and lime green.
The taste of gorgeous chunky chocolate in the winter.
It smells of appetising chips being cooked in the kitchen.
Sound of birds singing merrily early in the morning.
It's just like being happy and warm.
It looks just like an iced bun being eaten!

*Aimee Gilbourne (9)*
*Bramcote CE Primary School*

## FIRE

Fire
Flickering flames
People hurry out of houses
Children crying and crying
Everyone trying to get away
Blazing flames
Fire

*Faisal Khaliq (8)*
*Bramcote CE Primary School*

# FIRE

F lames flashing, flicking and banging everywhere. Quickly firemen.
I t's red, blue, yellow and orange and indigo, like a gigantic bonfire.
R oaring, raging, that's the sound. People fleeing away from the fire.
E veryone is upset because they have lost their friends and family.

*Rachel Murray (8)*
*Bramcote CE Primary School*

## MY BEST FRIEND

Me and my best friend are so very close.
We are nearly inseparable.
Even when we fall out.
It's only temperamental.

We hardly ever leave each other's side.
Only the weekends or holidays.
Even then we miss each other dearly.
But we still talk on the phone.
We try to keep in contact by mail or by phone.

There is no one thing that can separate us.
No person, or no one creature in the land.
That's been put on planet earth.
To separate our hands.

That's because I'm her best friend
And she is mine too, you know.
So no one can try.
Because we're best friends and that's true.

*Laura Attenborough (9)*
*Bramcote CE Primary School*

## ANGER

Anger is dark red and black.
The squishy taste of Brussel sprouts.
Anger is the smell of thick black smoke.
It sounds like polystyrene squeaking between my fingers.
Angry is bumpy and rough!

*Thomas Machin (9)*
*Bramcote CE Primary School*

## THE DIVER

I put on my aqua-lung and plunge,
To explore the deep blue sea,
Along my path I search and search,
I can hear myself breathing,
I can see sparks of glitter,
I'm surrounded by purple, green, blue, orange coral,
I can see a fish with brown stripes
And a yellow and blue after my side,
I have bubbles at my side,
I can see an old, dark, black, mysterious cave,
I think I knew what I'd see next,
It was an octopus sleeping,
I quickly swam away fast,
I go to the surface and swim back to the shore,
I am very cold.

*Liam Thorpe  (9)*
*Bramcote CE Primary School*




## ANGRY

Angry is light blinding red and I hardly ever want to see it.
Angry tastes like slippy slimy tomatoes
And I hate slippery slimy tomatoes.
It smells like around you,
Screeching and scratching cars skidding on the ice.
I want to get my own back on whoever or whatever did it.

*Umar Khaliq  (9)*
*Bramcote CE Primary School*

## THE DIVER

I put on my aqua-lung and plunge,
Exploring the vast, deep waters,
As clear as a polished crystal.
As I swam by, peach-coloured shells
Open and close, as if to say 'hello'.
I'm floating freely in the water, above red crabs
Which scuttle quickly sideways on
The glistening golden sand.
All round me is coral,
Infested with life,
Tiny fish, all colours of the rainbow.
Minute shrimps dart quickly
In and out of strangling slimy seaweed.
Look, a string of clear glass beads
Bubbling at my side, it's my breath!
Oh no, my air is running out,
Do I have to go and leave this relaxing
And trouble-free world?
I must.
I slowly swim to the surface,
Leaving behind the silence and the graceful fish,
Back to the noisy and ordinary world.

*Laura Davenport (10)*
*Bramcote CE Primary School*


## ANGER

Anger is dark red, black and bright pink.
The taste of Brussels sprouts squishy, disgusting.
It smells like compost in an old heap.
The sound of a bristly brush on a carpet.
It makes me feel *mad!*

*Oliver Thornton (9)*
*Bramcote CE Primary School*

## PARK BENCH DOG

Park bench dog with furball fluff,
Park bench dog scratching his ruff,
Sitting there with his decaying yellow teeth,
Gnawing his bone which used to be beef,
Looking at the world go by with his droopy brown eyes.

As people looked at his blood coloured scabs
Wondering if he wants any torn-up rags.
Just as he thought things were getting worse,
A lovely golden dog came up carrying a purse.
'Give it to me or I'll lash out my tail like
A tree branch in a fierce gale.'

His eyes were like thunder, her body was ready to attack,
*But*, they stopped, and all was calm, she handed the purse over,
And they walked side by side into the sunset.

*Olivia Wade  (10)*
*Bramcote CE Primary School*


## THE DIVER

I put on my aqua-lung and plunge into the deep blue sea,
I'm going to explore the ship beneath.
I look round like a scared pussy cat,
It's like a different world down here.
See the crabs crawling sideways.
Here we are at the bottom.
*Wow!* There's the ship, the old ship,
The old ship, there's the very old gold,
I had the gold, the old gold.

*Natasha Howe  (10)*
*Bramcote CE Primary School*

## FIREWORKS

Whizz, bang, pop,
Whizz, bang, pop.
Whoosh, bang,
Clatter, clang.

Scream and jig,
Scream and jig,
Screech and scorch,
As the crowd sing sang.

They serve right by,
Close to you.
As the crowd go wild,
Like animals in the zoo.

Fireworks,
Whizz, bang, pop!

*Amanda Truman  (10)*
*Bramcote CE Primary School*


## FAMILIES

Families can be all shapes and sizes.
They can be fat, thin, small, tall,
Big, round and funny.
Families can argue, play, shout,
Get cross and can be stressed.
Families can eat, sing, dance,
Prance, cook and squabble.
Families can be nice, sweet, cute,
Cuddly, friendly and happy.
Also families can be different.
What is your family like?

*Paige Martin  (8)*
*Bramcote CE Primary School*

# TEN LITTLE CHILDREN

Ten little children standing in a line
One fell over a cliff and then there were nine.

Nine little children at the school gate
Along came a roaring lion and then there were eight.

Eight little children travelling to Devon
One vanished in a puff of smoke and then there were seven.

Seven little children eating a Twix
One ate too much and then there were six.

Six little children standing on a hive
One got stung and then there were five.

Five little children standing by a door
One got hit and then there were four.

Four little children standing on a tree
One fell off and then there were three.

Three little children putting on a shoe
One got tangled up and then there were two.

Two little children eating a bun
One ate too much and then there was one.

One little child standing on a skateboard
Singing a song, he fell off
And then there were none.

*Nico Turner  (8)*
*Bramcote CE Primary School*

## SPRING!

On the 21st of March when you open door
Winter will be no more,
And when there's sun instead of snow or rain,
It means spring has come again.

Spring is the time when beautiful coloured flowers
Come out from their hiding in the ground,
And on the farm young newborn calves,
Piglets, lambs and chicks are to be found.

In the autumn leaves grow weary and drop
And leave the trees bare.
But in the spring leaves are growing
On trees everywhere.

*Richard Hanford  (10)*
*Bramcote CE Primary School*


## GUINEA PIGS ARE . . .

G   reedy, friendly guinea pigs
U   nhappy when they get no food,
I    n and out the hutch they scramble.
N   oisy guinea pigs.
E   verything they see, they eat!
A   pples which are bright red with chopped up carrots.

P   eople call them pigs but they're not!
I    n the hutch they are warm and dry,
G   reen grass they love to nibble,
S   ucking water out of their water bottles.

*Katie Davenport  (8)*
*Bramcote CE Primary School*

## THE SUN

Peeling my nose, reddening my skin
rising in the east, setting in the west
Bringing joy to frost-bitten people

　　Must be the sun
　　　　the sun
　　　　the sun

Smiling widely at the happy people
Enlightening their lives
Making everything golden

　　Must be the sun
　　the sun
　　the sun

*Lizzie Read  (10)*
*Bramcote CE Primary School*


## THE DIVER

I put on my aqua-lung and plunge,
Exploring, into the deep blue sea I go.
I see the black cave with octopus in it,
The tentacles, like a person lashing out in distress.
But I must take care, no I'm not scared,
Suddenly I see a sparkle on a coin,
It must be treasure, I'm rich, I'm rich *wahoo!*
I look at my timer, oh no I need to go up.

*Sam Dixon  (9)*
*Bramcote CE Primary School*

## LATE SPRING COUNTRYSIDE

Late spring countryside,
Frolicking lambs, prancing and dancing,
Their coats beautifully radiant, creamy, gleaming,
Going on rambles,
Playing hide and seek,
'Oh look, there's a rabbit! Just take a peek!'
I never want to leave fresh air and peace!
Oh well! Back to the city,
The cars and the fumes.
Oh I wish I could stay
Could stay!
Could stay!
Could stay!

*Annalise Grice (10)*
*Bramcote CE Primary School*


## THE WRECK

I put on my aqua-lung and got ready to plunge
I turned on my gear and *splash!*
I fell into the ocean of the Atlantic.
It's as silent as a grave. The fish swam past with
Bubbles coming out of its mouth.
As I touch the golden sand I discover a *wreck!*
As I enter the old, rusty ship I discover *gold!*
Gold can make me a fortune! I'll be *rich!*
As I look at my timer I only have *5 minutes left!*
So I leave the jewels and dive to the loud busy
World and live to tell the tale.

*Manpreet Singh Rakhra (10)*
*Bramcote CE Primary School*

## THE DIVER

I put on my aqua-lung
And plunge like a submarine
Yellow and bright down
In the deep I go. I see
Some treasure bright and
Gold. I see the sand yellow
As the sun. I see a shop
Wreck, old and mouldy.
I look through the porthole.
To my astonishment I see
A skeleton staring at me.
I swam back to the surface
Because I was frightened
Because I thought the
Skeleton was behind me.

*Steven Newcombe (10)*
*Bramcote CE Primary School*


## WHY?

Why does the tide change?
Why is fungi so strange?
Why do trees' leaves fall?
Why do birds call?
Why does the wind blow?
Why does the moon glow?
Why do dogs growl?
Why do wolves howl?
Why? Why? Why?

*Stephen Davis (10)*
*Bramcote CE Primary School*

## My Underwater Adventure

I calmly dived into the deep ocean blue,
firstly trying to avoid the hungry sharks
and also checking my regulator was in place.
The coral was beautiful,
reds, oranges, blues and greens,
as green as grass.
There were colourful fish,
all different shapes and sizes,
one yellow and green one
looked like a dull rainbow.
I saw a shipwreck overlooking
the ocean seabed, as misty and gloomy
as a bare cupboard.
I once again checked my regulator.
It was nearly empty.
All of a sudden I was back in the ordinary world.

*Jonathan Bryant  (9)*
*Bramcote CE Primary School*


## Fog

I look at the
miserable fog out on the hills.
Dragging its big grey cloak over
the land.
It swirls and twirls into every
nook and cranny.
Blocking people's view of the road.
Creeping to blind a poor passer-by.

*Jade Mellor  (9)*
*Bramcote CE Primary School*

## PARK BENCH DOG

Park bench dog lazily lying around
Park bench dog guarding his ground,
As round as a pig with stubby little legs
Pinching his eyes like little pegs.

Behold the sausage with shiny black nose
Leaning in his spot with a relaxed pose,
Staring from his droopy overlapped eyes
Looking up at the cloudy skies.

Park bench dog lazily lying around
Park bench dog guarding his ground.

*Chloe Martin (10)*
*Bramcote CE Primary School*


## SATs!

The SATs are here,
The stress is near.
Now it's time to revise,
For this terrible surprise.
We've done the test,
It's time to rest.
The scores are back,
All the teachers are sacked.

*Hayley Blake (10)*
*Brooksby Primary School*

## THE BOXER

I will do what no one has ever done
I will fly like a butterfly and sting like a bee
I will be undefeated
With a bit of training.

The fans will cheer for me
I will be the people's champ
I will be the champ for the people
I will be one of the people.

I will drive in a limousine
I will be rich
I will be rich with my fans
But for my family.

*Marc Watkins (9)*
*Brooksby Primary School*

## SICKY SATs!

The SATs are here,
It's time for me to disappear,
We've had time to revise,
But none of us have become wise.
We've started our test,
No time to rest,
I better finish quick,
Before I'm *sick!*

*Rebecca Blundell (11)*
*Brooksby Primary School*

# NIGHT TIME

It's night-time, it's night-time.
Outside it's getting dark,
People are wandering
Down to the park.

It's night-time, it's night-time
The moon outside is shining,
And in the great big houses
The families are dining.

It's night-time, it's night-time
I can hear someone weeping,
But it seems to me
That the world is sleeping.

It's morning, it's morning
The people awake
And people are wondering
Whether dreams are a fake!

*Jenny Kirby  (8)*
*Brooksby Primary School*


## VALENTINE'S POEM

I'll be your Romeo,
If you'll be my Juliet,
For you're so special,
You're hard to forget!
Your perfume;
Why does it smell so great?
If you'll accept my request,
Please don't be late!

*Matthew Mallek  (10)*
*Brooksby Primary School*

## THE DREADED SATS

The dreaded SATs have arrived
Our freedom they have just deprived
For just right now
We've started our test
With all the marks, who'll get the best
Oh no! I feel quite queasy
And my chest it's getting wheezy
Am I having an asthma attack
Or is it just a very bad back?
As the nursery plant a seed
Down my leg I've just . . .

*Alex Malcolm  (11)*
*Brooksby Primary School*


## SATS ARE HERE

SATs, SATs
How can you forget the SATs
When it pops up in your head
And lies upon your bed?
SATs rot my brain
Like the sewage drain
A feeling is in my tummy
I want to get away from here
Not even one little bit near
As time goes by, I want to cry
*I want my mummy!*

*Sharna Laskowski  (11)*
*Brooksby Primary School*

## A RECIPE TO MAKE A ... GUESS WHAT?

Squirts water,
coloured blue,
a long tail,
the tail has two points,
it has bright eyes,
its tail splashing madly,
a recipe to make a whale.

*Laura Kirby  (7)*
*Brooksby Primary School*

## MY CAT

My cat is so fat
As she goes along the road
She is kind alright
She walks around at night
And gives the mice a fright!

*Ciaran Townsend  (7)*
*Burton Joyce Primary School*

## DARKNESS

Darkness is the night
Darkness is big space
Darkness is a big black rainbow
Darkness is marching ants.

*Lydia Chrich  (7)*
*Burton Joyce Primary School*

## THE SPOOKY HOUSE!

Spooky house twirls round and round.
Rats squeaking, owls squawking,
Footsteps coming up the stairs.
What was that? What was that?
Slashing at the window tall, it's getting closer.
How could it be? Let's run quickly.
What, why, how!
Close the door, run away.
The shadow opened the door, *slash.*
Didn't you see the shadow following us everywhere?
That was only me!

*Luke Marsh  (7)*
*Burton Joyce Primary School*

## NAILS

Nails are big
Nails are small
Nails are spiky
Nails are tall
Nails are squodgy
Nails are thin
Nails are fat
Nails are dodgy!
But not all!

*Oliver Randall  (7)*
*Burton Joyce Primary School*

## MUSIC

Music, music everywhere,
Beats are floating in the air.
Saxophone and trumpet too,
I hope it doesn't stop too soon!

Bessy is playing the triangle.
Tim is getting in an awful tangle.
Amy is playing a brand new note,
1, 2, 3, now off you go.

Shosha is playing her new recorder,
Keep it up, the noise is getting smaller.
Eleanor and Charlotte doing duets,
You can't play this tune, I'll give you a bet.

*Robyn Dickson  (9)*
*Burton Joyce Primary School*


## THE WORLD IS A FOOTBALL

The world is a football
A beautiful old football
It's green and blue
There's a splendid match
Going on right now.
God is the excellent striker
And Jesus is the goalkeeper
Who do you think will win?
I don't know.
Do you?

*Daniel Roberts  (7)*
*Burton Joyce Primary School*

## WINTER

Snow, snow everywhere on the ground.
Icy silver going round.
Freezing cold, swirling round.
Snow, snow, everywhere going in your hair.
It's going round, it's freezing cold.
It's swirling round.
The two little birds in the snow.
They're freezing cold and wet as well.

*Olivia Wallace  (8)*
*Burton Joyce Primary School*


## THE MONSTER

Teeth crunching
Mouth munching
Eyes lighting
Hands fighting
Tail dragging
Stop nagging!

*Richard Whipps  (9)*
*Burton Joyce Primary School*


## MY IMAGINARY ROBOT

He has a shiny copper-plated body.
He has two brass arms.
He has metal legs.
He sometimes goes rusty in the rain.

*Steven Dixon  (9)*
*Burton Joyce Primary School*

## CHOCOLATE

Chocolate is hot, chocolate is mmm!
Chocolate will melt in a very hot room.
Chocolate is thin, chocolate is fat.
Chocolate is nice and that is a fact.
Chocolate is yummy for my tummy.
Chocolate is creamy, it is so yummy.

*Stacey Marshall  (8)*
*Burton Joyce Primary School*


## TOOTHPASTE

Different shapes,
Sizes,
Colours,
And even makes!
It fluffs up in your mouth
*Wooh!*
That's strong!

*Alex Smith  (8)*
*Burton Joyce Primary School*


## WIND

It waves round me, blowing with anger.
A sudden gentle breeze, wrapping itself around me.
I breathe in some air, refreshing me after long, hot days.
It was swaying and whistling in the trees.
Suddenly the trees tremble.
A sign of danger, a storm is coming!

*India Boddy  (8)*
*Burton Joyce Primary School*

## HOT AND COLD

Hot and cold colours get on your nerves,
'Cause when you turn around
They're there on the curve.
Hot and cold colours are very nice,
But when you try to eat them
They turn to ice.
Hot and cold colours some are scorching,
Roasting and toasting.
Hot and cold are very funny
'Cause when you turn around
It's there faster than a zooming greyhound.

*Lee Cawser  (8)*
*Burton Joyce Primary School*

## SLEEPY THE DOG

Asleep he is by the fire.
Never waking to scratch his fleas.
He never awakes to eat his food.
He never likes to be groomed.
He likes a bone by his side and
A bowl of milk.
He has a black nose that is not to be touched.
But he's never awake.

*Charlotte Randall  (9)*
*Burton Joyce Primary School*

## DARKNESS

Darkness is starless,
Darkness is black,
Darkness is gloomy,
Darkness is shadowy,
Darkness is shady,
Darkness is sunless,
Darkness is unlit,
Darkness is black soot,
Darkness is spooky,
Darkness is the night sky,
Darkness is black sugar paper,
Darkness is the black fur of a panther.

*Eleanor Stevenson  (9)*
*Burton Joyce Primary School*


## PLAYING IN WATER

Girls moaning
   Boys groaning
Mums shouting
   Dogs barking
Cars crashing
   Girls skipping
Men swearing
   Babies crying
Mums beebing
   Children screaming
People splashing
   Children wafting!

*Emma Kelvey  (7)*
*Burton Joyce Primary School*

## TREES, TREES EVERYWHERE

Trees that are green,
Trees that are brown,
Trees that are knobbly,
Trees that are bare,
Trees that are thin,
Trees that are fat,
Trees that are dull,
Trees that are bright,
Trees that are beautiful,
Trees that are horrible,
Trees that are dead,
Trees that are alive,
Trees that are round,
It is so hard to explain how many trees there are.

*Emma Collins  (7)*
*Burton Joyce Primary School*

## FUNNY HANDS

Hands can clap and flap,
Hands can be all sorts of colours.
Hands can riddle and fiddle,
Hands can wriggle.
Hands can squeeze and tease,
Hands can write and have frights.
Hands have wiggly fingers like silly sausages,
Hands with colourful patterns.

*Eleanor Cope  (7)*
*Burton Joyce Primary School*

## ALIEN PREDATOR

A long head,
A mouth that comes out of another mouth,
Claws that stick into walls,
A gun on its left spiky shoulder,
A controller on its bloody left arm,
His legs move like lightning,
A tail with a point at the end,
He has no eyes, but his smell is excellent.

*Jacob Springthorpe (7)*
*Burton Joyce Primary School*

## SPRING!

In the spring, the flowers bloom.
Lots of colours, lots of fun.
Baby rabbit playing in sun.
The fox is sneaking, yes it is.
Baby rabbit now all gone!

Buds bloom in the sun.
Lots of colours, lots of fun.
Lambs bleating, being born
And the corn, of course
Golden yellow like the sun.

*Ella Marriott (8)*
*Burton Joyce Primary School*

## THE DRAGON

I ran as I saw it,
Then I went back.
It was a tiny dragon,
Just the size of a bird.
It had little blue eyes,
Looking at me sweetly.
As I got closer,
It purred!
I stroked its golden spines,
It was mostly silver.
Its whole body glistened,
In the golden sun.
Its long tail curled around,
Into a spiral.
Its breath smelt like yellow lilies.
She picked a little daisy for me,
Then she winked!
I knelt down,
And patted her smooth, silver head.
She was beautiful!

*Esther Rigg  (8)*
*Burton Joyce Primary School*


## SNOW, SNOW, BRILLIANT STUFF

Children wading across the deep milky white snow.
Snowy snowflakes fill the ground.
Bare trees stand out against the dark grey sky,
Their branches bowing low.

*Joseph Roberts  (8)*
*Burton Joyce Primary School*

## CHRISTMAS ON THE FRONT LINE

The fields drenched in blood,
the guns disabled,
but it seems to be silent.
How can this be?
Only yesterday, there were cries
from the brave soldiers who were
protecting this battery,
now just silence,
but soon these guns shall fire again
but this time the heart filled cries
of peace shall roar once more and
the guns shall fire shells of thanks.

The year is 1914, Christmas.

*Ted Mills (8)*
*Burton Joyce Primary School*

## THE DRAGON

I was walking home when,
I saw a green thing,
Dropping from the sky,
It hit the ground.

Its eyes were like the sun,
With small red wings and scaly silver body,
It was as big as a cat.

Then I thought, what was it?

*Joshua Keyworth (9)*
*Burton Joyce Primary School*

## THE DRAGON

The dragon is coming to town
He's coming, yes, he's coming, I can see him.
He's coming through the streets, aaaahhhh!
He's got red eyes gleaming at me in the sunlight.
He's got razor sharp teeth like a jagged knife.
With a green scaly back, he has a big swishing tail
Which smashes houses down.
He has purple spikes sticking out of his back.
He can breathe fire, now he's roasted the houses.
They're just little bits of dust.

*Christopher Andrew Jackson (7)*
*Burton Joyce Primary School*


## THE DRAGON

I saw a twinkle
It pounced at me.
Fear flowed down my spine.
It was as small as a cup,
Its back was silky,
His eyes were blazing
Its nails where as long
As a sharpened sword.
It purred with joy,
It hissed with fear,
I couldn't believe my eyes!
A dragon by my side.

*Thomas William Jones (8)*
*Burton Joyce Primary School*

## MY PET DOG

When I first saw it
Curled up in the corner
Guess what it was
My pet *dog*
With its wet and cold nose
And fur as soft as a horse
As small as a baby
As cute as a duckling
My pet dog was here
*At last.*

**Roxanne Hickling  (8)**
**Burton Joyce Primary School**


## THE JUNGLE

Snakes hissing,
Tigers growling,
Crocodiles snapping,
Monkeys screaming,
Hippos yawning,
Lizards spitting,
Elephants shouting,
Cheetahs sneaking,
Then king of the jungle
Lions roaring.

**Alex Craddock  (8)**
**Burton Joyce Primary School**

## GHOSTS

I believe in ghosts
It's really very simple
They only come out at night
So you wouldn't have seen them
They're white and clear
They're very spooky
I've not met one
But I think they're really cool
And one thing more
They go
*boo!*

*Ria Fearn  (9)*
*Burton Joyce Primary School*



## MY MOUSE

Eyes like black beads.
Ears like ham.
His tail is like bacon rind and
Oh, his golden body
So shiny like gold.
He pokes his nose out from his bed.
Climbing on the cage.
That's my mouse!

*Leigh Quarry  (8)*
*Burton Joyce Primary School*

## UNDER THE BED

As I lay in bed,
I wonder if it's there.
As I lay at night,
I hear it howling and wailing.
When I look under the bed,
I see his red evil eyes.
I hear him growling and wailing,
But I don't know why he cries.
I think he's hurt himself,
But who cares, he hides.

*Peter Olbrecht  (8)*
*Burton Joyce Primary School*

## NOVEMBER

November is like a world of snow
that's flying through the air.
The snow is like a crystal
jumping tree to tree.
If you stick the snowflakes together
you can make a picture.
But some day you will see
there isn't any snow.
Now it is a different month, it is
*December!*

*Eleanor Williams  (8)*
*Burton Joyce Primary School*

## THE SKELETON DRIVE

Who is driving
an invisible car
with power steering
and armoured grey doors,
a serpent on your neck?
Anyway how do you stay alive
without a heart?

*Aaron Singh  (8)*
*Burton Joyce Primary School*


## MY ISLAND

As I walked upon the sea,
I saw an island,
In front of me.

I found some treasure,
that filled me with pleasure.
Gold and silver,
just for me.

*Hayley Elizabeth Glover  (9)*
*Burton Joyce Primary School*


## LOST

I was in the middle of nowhere,
Nothing to keep me warm,
No torch or any food to cook,
Lonely, yes I was.

Dressed in animal clothing,
I wish I was in England,
Nobody's coming to rescue me,
I don't have anything.

*William Phipps (7)*
*Burton Joyce Primary School*

# RAIN

On one big sad day,
Rain came down,
After the rain,
There were big
Puddles on the ground.
They were like a flowing steam.

*Aimee R Tozer (9)*
*Burton Joyce Primary School*

# PIRANHA

Its belly is raging red
Its teeth a razor sharp
It tears, it rips, it bites
Until its prey dies of shock
It has a ravenous appetite
It kills its prey with razors
Its teeth can gnaw and strip
A bone until it snaps in half.

*Thomas Parker (8)*
*Burton Joyce Primary School*

## Dog

If I could be reincarnated I'd be a dog
With long furry hair and warm body inside
Lots of dog biscuits in my juicy dinner
Rabbit taste would be for me.

Eating lots of left-overs after a party night
Getting lots of treats every day when I am good
White fur with big brown patches on top
Big clean white teeth to dig into meat.

Going out for lots of long walks
Always chasing balls and sticks
When people throw them over my head
My tail always wagging even when I am sitting
I would live in a warm place
Lying by the fire all day and night.

*Aimee Wallis (8)*
*Chetwynd Road Primary School*


## I Don't Like

I don't like mustard,
It makes me hot,
But I do like custard,
Served in a pot.

I don't like ham,
It makes me sick,
But I do like spam,
With a big lick.

*Danielle Guyatt (8)*
*Chetwynd Road Primary School*

## COBRA

If I could be reincarnated I'd be a cobra
With scaly skin, my patterned frill would
Shine in the blazing sun.
When my prey would come it would look up
Then I would hypnotise my prey and eat it.

Next I see a deer eating some plants
It does not see me.
Suddenly it looks up
It backs away, then it runs.

It gets dark in the sky, bats swoop overhead
I head back to my hole.
Then I swiftly slither into my hole.

*Edward Coates  (8)*
*Chetwynd Road Primary School*

## POLAR BEAR

If I could be reincarnated I'd be a polar bear.
This is because I'd like to have as white as snow fur.
I'd shake the cold, wet water from my low body.
And no-one would know I was there.
My icy cold feet would dig into the ice as I walk along.
I would wait for my meat and then I'd eat my lovely treat.
I'd like to chase a seal until it hides behind a rock.
I'd swim and swim and swim until I find a grey, old, rusty lock.
I would have a camouflaged coat to keep me warm in the snow.
If someone tried to catch me, I'd hide under their wooden boat.

*Victoria McQueen  (9)*
*Chetwynd Road Primary School*

## MEETING A GHOST

A ghost floated through a dusty wall
I thought he would like to play ball
I said, 'How do you do it?' and he said back
'Why don't you jump into my huge sack?'

'Oh very good do it again
Other clowns are really a pain.'
The ghost started to clatter and clang,
The silver chains made a really big bang.

I shouted out, 'Encore! Encore!'
The ghost thought he was very poor
He started to go away,
I said, 'Come back another day,'

*Ellen Phillips  (8)*
*Chetwynd Road Primary School*


## MEETING A GHOST

Mrs Mayson and Tina Biscuit,
Bought a castle, and got a ghost with it,
So this is how the story goes,
And it is sure to tickle your toes.

One evening when they were sitting down to dine,
Something made Mrs Mayson drop her wine,
But young Tina, quick and clever,
Was going to make sure, the ghost was gone forever.

And so with a shriek and a howl,
Which made it sound like an owl,
He went, and that was quite hearty,
Tina Biscuit and Mrs Mayson had a party.

*Rachel Baker  (8)*
*Chetwynd Road Primary School*

## MEETING A GHOST

A ghost haunted Spooky Terror House,
When I went there it was as quiet as a mouse.
Then it growled and roared,
And it was carrying a sword.

It went through walls,
Howled round doors.
I called merrily at it, 'That was fine.
Have a bit of sherry wine.'

Furious with rage,
The ghost exchanged,
Himself for dine.
I chuckled and said, 'This house is mine!'

*Elizabeth Bovey  (8)*
*Chetwynd Road Primary School*


## MEETING A GHOST

One foggy night I met a ghost,
I said, 'Excuse me, have some toast.'
The ghost sat down and looked with his eye,
I said, 'My dear fellow, let's do eye spy.'

The ghost haunted me with his chains
I said, 'Hey you nice blood veins.'
The ghost was furious,
I said, 'Hey, are you serious?'

The ghost was so mad,
He started being bad,
I said, 'Do stay.'
But the ghost just flew away.

*Joe Cook  (8)*
*Chetwynd Road Primary School*

## MEETING A GHOST

Colonel Custard Cocktail Flare,
Found a ghost in his underwear,
But he was not scared at all,
He just walked off down the hall.

The ghost began to moan and grown,
Thought he could scare colonel out of his home,
The colonel just laughed and then he said,
'How do you do it? I must go to bed.'

The ghost, oh yes was quite upset,
His tears came out, but he didn't get wet,
He had never, not scared someone before,
So he just vanished through the floor.

*Suzanne Morrice  (8)*
*Chetwynd Road Primary School*


## I DON'T LIKE

I don't like salmon
And I don't like melon
I don't like gammon
But I do like lemon

I don't like coffee
And I don't like ham
But I do like toffee
Even if it is with jam

I don't like mussels
And I don't like beef
I do like Brussels
But they break my teeth.

*Chloe Prior  9)*
*Chetwynd Road Primary School*

## MEETING A GHOST

Captain Jimilin Earthworm Apple,
Was sitting comfortable upon the settee,
When down came a spectre,
My! He did get a lecture.

'You should not do that!'
Captain Jim boomed,
'You'll scare people out of their wits,
And, don't you even bother, shaking yourself to bits!'

At this poor shade,
(Nothing else up his sleeve)
Left the old house,
Like a little scared mouse.

So Captain Jimilin Earthworm Apple,
Went upstairs and got into bed,
Then remembering the poor ghost weep,
Captain Jimilin drifted off to sleep.

*Stephen Laing (9)*
*Chetwynd Road Primary School*


## JAMES BOND

James Bond walking down the streets looking to help people to survive.
Goes past houses, burglars go by.
James Bond can get them on the double
Now if a man gets you in trouble
He'll be in on the double.
Guarantee he'll be heading for 6. Goes travelling the world.
It's just like he's invincible, he's the best.
So beware, he can do it any day and any way.

*Lewis Cracknell (9)*
*Coddington Primary & Nursery School*

## WEEKS

Weeks go drifting by
Never get a chance to
See the river trickling
Silently by.

Sat inside doing my endless
Homework that I collected
That day.
When I have finished it's time for tea
And then to bed.

That's why I never see the
River trickling by and by.

*Laura Daubney  (9)*
*Coddington Primary & Nursery School*


## BIG OR SMALL

Big as a dinosaur
    Small as a snail
Big as a house
    Small as a pea
Big as a giant
    Small as me, 3 feet
Big as a tree
    Small as a rock
Big as a planet
    Small as a snail
Big as a cow
    Small as a kitten

*Joe Mastin  (9)*
*Coddington Primary & Nursery School*

## DANGER, DANGER

Animals are in danger,
    danger we all hate.
Animals are in danger,
    they don't like it either.
Sea horses are dying out,
    just because of us.
They don't do us any harm,
    but we harm them, their lives.
Animals are in danger,
    danger we all hate.
Animals are in danger,
    they don't like it either.
There are animals all over the world,
    some are alright.
But most are dying out,
    that gives me a fright.
I don't like fox hunting or,
    whale killing or rabbits or snakes.
Now my poem is nearly over,
    so all I have to say is
*Please leave them alone!*

*Carrie-Anne Pollard  (9)*
*Coddington Primary & Nursery School*


## IN THE MORNING

When I wake up in the morning
I see leaves rustling.
And I see the clouds gently drifting.
And I hear the wind whispering.

*Nicola Marriott  (9)*
*Coddington Primary & Nursery School*

## ABOUT ME

Sometimes I think there's just me,
I think I'm the only one here.
Sometimes I think I'm a bee,
Gently floating in the air.

When I'm all alone I feel like a mole,
Digging underground
Just using my nose to guide me.
Then I feel like a worm
Jumping in a hole to
Protect myself from a
Bird trying to get me.

Then at the end of the day,
I feel like a squirrel just
About to curl asleep in a tree.
So that is the end of my poor sad day,
And that s all I have told you about me.

*Kalon Lowe  (9)*
*Coddington Primary & Nursery School*


## DAYS

Sometimes I dream
About a stream
Gently drifting across the rocks
Then suddenly the trees rustled like mad
As the people watching this feel bad
The wind rushing past me whispering in my ear.

*Jack Beckett  (8)*
*Coddington Primary & Nursery School*

## THE KINGFISHER

The kingfisher, you can see him high,
He stalks his prey,
As he launches off the branch,
He swoops down to his prey,
In a flash he's gone,
Gone back up to the branch,
Feasting on his prey,
Later he glides through the air,
To his territory,
And there he stays,
For the night,
Until dawn,
He has a peaceful night,
No enemies come to attack,
(They probably don't dare).
So enemies beware!

*Amy Collins  (9)*
*Coddington Primary & Nursery School*


## SUNLIGHT

Sunlight in the morning
Creeps up without any warning
Making sure the day is light
And then like us she sleeps at night
Making sure the day is fine
She works so hard to shine ~ shine ~ shine
When it's time to rest at night
She disappears out of sight
And then like clockwork up she pops
Over hills, trees and chimney pots.

*Ruth Daybell  (9)*
*Coddington Primary & Nursery School*

## SPOOKCHESTER MANOR

Vampires strike deep in the night.
Every soul gets a fright.
Sharp fangs and a cape.
Everybody tries to escape.
They are so sly.
They can fly in the sky.

They had some rivals called the zombies who died.
Their coffins are open, people get terrified.
They have a hobby of roaming streets.
Walks right into whatever it meets.
They walk around and dance.
The darkness puts them in a trance.

*Marcus Young  (9)*
*Coddington Primary & Nursery School*


## I AM

I am peaceful.
I am drifting in the sky.
I am calm.
I am dreamy in bed.
I am whispering to Kyle.
I am gawping in my bedroom.
I am looking at a cat.
I am looking out of my window.
I am singing in the rain.
My mum went home singing in the rain.
My brother is sad in bed.
My little brother Aaron is happy at school learning.

*Alyssa Moody  (9)*
*Coddington Primary & Nursery School*

## WITH PEOPLE

When I am alone,
I feel very sad,
I don't feel that I can speak loudly.
I feel I have to speak in a whisper,
Sometimes I think no one cares about me,
I even think that no one loves me,
Being alone isn't very nice.

When I am with people I appreciate it,
I feel very happy,
I feel I can speak proudly,
Not in a whisper,
Then I feel people love me and care for me,
I like being with people.

*Catherine Carter (9)*
*Coddington Primary & Nursery School*


## FEELINGS

The sun is about to rise
And I have just woken
I'm sad I've got to go back to school
And I have not even spoken

As soon as it is playtime
The rain starts to drizzle
As soon as I go inside
I watch the classroom sizzle

When I'm in the classroom
I watch till I'm drenched
With soaking up what's going on
And I'm fainting . . . fainting . . . fainting.

*Craig Jackson (9)*
*Coddington Primary & Nursery School*

## FANTASTIC MR FOX

Mr Fox asks his wife,
'What is it tonight my dear?'
Over the tree he peers,
To see if anything is near.

Mrs Fox replies, 'Chicken please.'
'Chicken it shall be.'
And when Mr Fox has gone,
She thinks, 'Oh! What a lad is he.'

He leaves is wife and children,
To find a nice beast,
When he comes back,
Oh what a feast!

But those creatures,
Boggis, Bunce and Bean,
With their guns,
*Ooh!* They are so mean.

Bean is a turkey and apple farmer,
He is the cleverest of them all,
He drinks a lot of apple cider,
And is also very tall.

Bunce is a duck and goose farmer,
His food is doughnuts and liver,
He makes a disgusting paste,
When he eats it I bet it makes him quiver.

Boggis is a chicken farmer,
He keeps thousands of chickens,
He has dumplings every day,
And before he has them he has his lips licking.
I hope you have enjoyed this lovely rhyme,
Maybe I can see you next time.

*Rose Allen  (9)*
**Coddington Primary & Nursery School**


## DEATH

I'm locked in a gigantic castle,
It's frightening,
Bells ring in my head,
As I walk on through the castle,
I shiver and feel cold.

I come to a door that I open,
I feel alone and want to weep,
Silently as ever I go in,
And kneel and start to cry
I tell God about the things I regret feeling awful.

It's torture, it's horrible,
I feel pain near my heart,
And my head is thumping,
It's shocking and frightening,
Flames appear around me,
But now it's all over now,
I feel small,
When I look small,
*Am I dead?*

*Sarah King  (9)*
**Coddington Primary & Nursery School**

## ONE WEIRD DAY

One Thursday morning I woke up and saw
It was a bear with a massive paw
I got out of bed and ran downstairs
I saw my mum and dad there were several pairs
I ran back upstairs and went into the bathroom
When I got in it was black, it was doom
I got dressed and went to school
That day wasn't very cool
I got to school and everyone said,
'You haven't brushed your hair. What's on your head?'
The bell went, we went in
When we sat down we sat on a pin
In class we learnt take aways and adds
At hometime the parents picking us up, mostly the dads
I got home, I sat down
Mum was out, she was at town
My dad was in the living room
He was watching TV, two people were getting married, a bride and
       groom
I went upstairs and looked at a book
Mum came in, she put her coat on a hook
Mother shouted, 'Dinner time.'
But brother was on a crime
I had my tea and went to bed
I put my head on the pillow, my pillow is red.

*Rebecca Turner  (9)*
*Coddington Primary & Nursery School*

## FEELINGS ABOUT DIFFERENT DAYS

Sometimes days are *mad!*
*Angry* thunder clouds gather up in the sky.
The rain *crashes* down, dancing on the road!
When it's a *mad, rainy* day, I feel
*Angry, excited* and *bouncy!*
Yet, when it's a bright day
I feel calm, peaceful, silent and dreamy.
The blazing sun is burning,
I feel happy on sunny days.
On sad days when I'm alone I feel
Nobody wants me.
I feel mournful.

*Hayley Verrills  (9)*
*Coddington Primary & Nursery School*


## CAR

If I had a car
What would it be?

It would be every boy's dream car
One to pull the girl's car
Super turbo sports car
Long and sleek car
Clean and gleaming car
Bright red car
For everyone to see car
To get the neighbour's net curtains twitching car
Bring stares from everyone car
0-60 in seconds car
But most of all it would be my car

*Michael Paul Chapman  (9)*
*Crompton View Primary School*

## FOOTBALL'S COMING HOME!

Football is the best,
Better than all the rest,
Man United play in red,
Wake up sleepy heads, then get out of bed,
We queue to get into the stand,
Don't push or you'll trap my hand.
    'Football's coming home!'
In the stand we're at the back,
Gee, thank God for that,
There's bottles and cans in the air,
I'm so glad we're not down there,
The game begins, the whistle blows,
Silence everywhere, it only shows.
    'Football's coming home!'
The crowd make me jump, what a din,
I looked away, oh no, the ball went in.
It's one nil to the other team,
It really makes me want to scream,
The ball is down at Man U's end,
So come on Beckham, make it bend,
    'Football's coming home!'
It's a draw, who will be their best?
This match will put them to the test,
The players fight and squabble,
One player's hurt, he's got a wobble,
Come on lads, it's nearly time,
Wait Ref, we're doing fine.
    *'Football's coming home!'*

*Scott Marshall  (10)*
*Crompton View Primary School*

## MY FRIEND

My friend is mean,
though she's won all her races,
and gone through her paces.
When you go to her house on baking day,
quite meanly she asks you to pay.
When she goes to a meeting,
she gives no one a greeting.

Her skin is thin,
everyone thinks, 'She's got horrid skin.'
She's never behaving,
and she's bad at bathing!
She's got a cat,
but spanks it for sleeping in her hat!
She's ripped up her robe,
and throws away her globe!
She brings out no dinner on a tray,
and says, 'No dinner for you today!'
I've got to agree,
she's even a dog, for she eats Pedigree!

*Zelie Wardle  (9)*
*Crompton View Primary School*

## TWINKLE, TWINKLE

Twinkle, twinkle chocolate bar
My dad drives a rusty car.
Pull the trigger, turn the key.
My dad goes off in a puff of smoke.

*Jodi Lunn  (9)*
*Crompton View Primary School*

## MY FRIEND

I like tidy rooms,
My friend likes messy rooms.
I like quiet,
My friend likes noisy.
I like books,
My friend doesn't.
I like videos,
My friend likes TV.
I like to sleep,
My friend is always awake.
I like school,
My friend hates it.
I like my teacher,
My friend does not.
I like maths and English,
My friend likes pie.

*Louise Bowling  (9)*
*Crompton View Primary School*


## THE SNOWMAN

The snowman in the garden stands,
With two old sticks made for hands,
An told top hat upon his head,
In his mouth a pipe of lead,
A coat and scarf to keep him warm,
Against the cold and winter storm,
Up against the wall he'll stay,
Until the sun melts him away.

*Natalie Bates  (9)*
*Crompton View Primary School*

## PETS

What is a pet, is it a dog or a cat?
A hamster or rat?
I have a dog called Peggy,
She's loving and giving, cute and sweet,
I take her for walks down the street.

What is a pet, is it a dog or a cat?
A hamster or rat?
I have a cat called Tufty,
I sit her on my knee away from harm,
She's so soft and smooth, cuddly and warm.

What is a pet, is it a dog or a cat?
A hamster or rat?
I'd like a hamster called Harry,
I'd play with him, while I drank my milk,
Because he's small and cute with fur like silk.

What is a pet, is it a dog or a cat?
A hamster or rat?
I'd like a rat called Zach,
He'd scurry around and around in a gale,
His fur flashing by with his very long tail.

*Adrian Leach (10)*
*Crompton View Primary School*


## MAN U

A team called Man U
They play football. They are good.
I support their team.

*Ryan Dixon (10)*
*Crompton View Primary School*

# A WILDLIFE POEM

Giraffes, they have a purplish tongue, legs so thin and mighty long.
They feed on leaves from trees so high, what a long neck! Now I know
why.
Elephants, their ears are large and flappy, to roll in the mud, makes
them extremely happy!
The hippo, however, he's lazy and less fun, he floats in the water and
basks in the sun.
Monkeys, they like to climb and to swing, the chimpanzee, he is an
intelligent thing!
Happy to groom each other for fleas, doing each day just whatever they
please.
The Snake, he is long and so very sly, sleeping all day, whilst the time
ticks on by.
People, they think he is slimy and cold, but they're really quite warm, if
you dare take a hold!
The king of the jungle, it's the lion for sure, he's evil, ferocious, need I
tell you some more?
Guarding his territory, by day and by night, if you get too close, he'll
give you a fright!
But as evening arrives, and the jungle becomes still, you can bet there is
something waiting to kill?
The fox likes await with his bushy red tail, his dinner in sight, a juicy
fat quail.

*Emmely Dovaston  (9)*
*Crompton View Primary School*


## MY LITTLE SISTER

My little sister,
Who is such a little pain
Bites me all the time.

*Michaela Richardson  (10)*
*Crompton View Primary School*

## WILD POEMS

W ildlife
I  wonder
L  ife in the countryside
D  ragonflies they slumber.
L  ife in the countryside
I  wonder
F  lying through the air
E  lephants taking care.

The old king of Dorchester,
He had an orchestra,
And never did you hear
Such a ceremonial band.

The jungle bells ring because the hyenas
Are dancing in the ring.

*Stefan Karl Prest  (10)*
*Crompton View Primary School*


## IT'S A MYSTERY?

Beneath the fields and beneath the skies lay mysteries and
fisteries of ancient times of Romans and Stonemen.
Beneath the grass lay beetles and birds, and animal treasures
and much more to be curse.
Beneath the universe lay planets and stars, black holes
and more to be told.
Under the sea are fishes and sharks much more than larks,
have sensitive reactions and sensitive jaws.
So just remember the mysteries that lay not far
from far within anywhere like our cars.

*Reece Tonkinson  (10)*
*Crompton View Primary School*

## NUTTY NEIGHBOURS

My crazy neighbours who live next door
Whose names are Roger and Joyce
They're always doing silly things
And Joyce has a high-pitched voice.

My dad goes round to their house
I find it rather queer
He always goes round at night
To have a drink of beer.

They're always having barbecues
For everyone to see
Everyone seems to be having fun
It's always boring for me.

Roger likes to make cocktails
He says, 'A bit of this and a bit of that.'
Joyce is in charge of the cooking
But I give mine to the cat.

*Rebecca Whetton  (9)*
*Crompton View Primary School*


## MONKEYS

Monkeys climb up trees,
Some check themselves for fleas,
They run up and down,
Some fall on the ground,
With a very loud pound.

Monkeys eat bananas,
Monkeys dream bananas,
Monkeys go bananas.

Oh yes! Oh yes,
It's that time again,
Running, crashing, clowning around,
But soon once more it's time for bed,
As they dream bananas in their heads.

*Michael Mitchell (10)*
*Crompton View Primary School*


## ROCKET BLAST

5, 4, 3, 2, 1, up, up and away
watch our rocket zoom and sway

Up to Mars we go, go, go
people on earth are down, down low

When we get to Mars, Mars, Mars
we will get some candy bars, bars, bars

I'm on my own in this rocket
not really, I've got my hamster in my pocket

I want to meet a man on Mars, Mars, Mars
I've got a friend there called Twinkle Stars, Stars, Stars

I'm nearly there, there, there
I hope I don't give the aliens a scare, scare, scare

Now I'm on Mars and I've heard the news
I'm going to have a snooze zzzzzzz.

*Ella Lawrence-Cowling (9)*
*Elston All Saints Primary School*

# THE SECRET MEETING PLACE

Up there in space
Is a secret place

Where all the aliens meet
All of them have 13 feet

And 15 eyes
They also wear ties

Their hair is yellow
And they love marshmallow

The secret place
Is made of lace

They all have the same name
And hide and seek is their favourite game

Their hands are the size of mops
And their leader is flops

So hanging in the middle of space
Is the secret place made of lace

*Sophie Beever  (10)*
*Elston All Saints Primary School*


# A THING FROM SPACE

There was a man from space
Who had a very ugly face

So when he landed on land
He said he was very, very grand

I am going to die soon
So I have to go back to the moon

I have to go to bed
Or I will lose my head
And then I will be dead

I have to leave now
Or I will turn into a space cow
So bye-bye for now

*Matthew Newcombe  (9)*
*Elston All Saints Primary School*

## SPACE WARS

We're the Remuns
And they are the Gemuns

We fight for freedom
They fight for wisdom

Our spacecraft is round
And it's low to the ground

We fight around in our spacecrafts
There's a slight draught

But we can call them the meanees
And they call us weanees

Our side has tanks
But we do not have a rank

The war goes on and on
But sometimes we win

*James Clarke  (10)*
*Elston All Saints Primary School*

## SCWIGLE IN SPACE

There's a bong in space, bong, bong,
There's a flit in space, flit, flit.
But the weirdest is the Scwigle in space.

There's a lifpuf in space, lifpuf, lifpuf,
There's a wonker in space, wonker, wonker.
But the weirdest is the Scwigle in space.

There's a glop in space, glop, glop,
There's a nomp in space, nomp, nomp.
But the weirdest is . . .
There's a bumbo in space, bumbo, bumbo,
There's a flipo in space, flipo, flipo.
But the weirdest is . . .

There's a wooot in space, wooot, wooot,
There's a lit in space, lit, lit.
But the weirdest is . . .

There's a zop in space, zop, zop,
There's a eleitry in space, eleitry, eleitry.
But the weirdest is . . .

What a pretty, pretty dream,
I shall never forget that Scwigle in space.
Never, never, never.

*Alan Freer  (11)*
*Elston All Saints Primary School*

## MY DAYS IN SPACE

I had two weeks and a day in space,
It's such a lovely place.
There's aliens, planets and stars,
And my story starts on Mars.

I came to Mars, the planet red,
I met an alien, he said,
'You are on the planet Mars,
Come and eat some candy bars.'

He offered me some food,
But I was a bit rude.
I ran away,
For a week and a day.

Everywhere I hid,
When he found me I felt like a small kid.
He was very kind,
And didn't mind.

He offered me some coke,
And told me a joke.
We went to the moon,
And very soon,

We went on another
Adventure to find his mother.
We found her in Rome,
And then I went home.

So some time in space,
Made me know it's a funny place.
There's aliens, planets and stars,
But my favourite planet is *Mars!*

*Charlotte Crowson  (9)*
*Elston All Saints Primary School*

# ROCKETS!

Zoom! Zoom! Rockets whizzing around Mars
just like racing cars.

Singing fire
like the choir.

5, 4, 3, 2, 1, blast off, smoke performs clouds
like massive crowds.

As rockets whizz past the moon
they go all loony!

As rockets zoom everywhere, the fire performs beams
you hear shooting stars scream!

When the rocket cracks
glue with Pepsi Max.

As rockets whizz past Jupiter
they get more stupider.

Rockets are better
than all the rest!

*Adam Hill (9)*
*Elston All Saints Primary School*

# I Went Up In My Spaceship

I went up in my spaceship
Just guess what I saw?
A great gathering of aliens strewn on the floor
Some were red and some were blue
But not one of them looked like you
Some were yellow and some were green
They were the wildest thing I've ever seen

I went up in my spaceship
Oh what a sight
I saw an alien make a big bike
Its eyes were purple but were pink
Its head was covered in brown ink
Its legs were as long as Jack's beanstalk
And its stomach was like pork

I went down in my spaceship
Back down to Earth
This is the place I had my birth
Everyone looks like aliens now
Even Daisy, my brown cow.

*John Gunstone (10)*
*Elston All Saints Primary School*

## SPACE RAP

Yo! I'm going to tell you a space rap!
(Quite fast)

In a deep dark planet,
there's an alien called Janet,
Janet has a cat,
its name was Pat.

Pat is a cat,
that loves to eat rats,
and loves Postman Pat,
how about that!

Pat has a flea,
which is really itchy,
the flea never has a bath,
who knows why he runs a cafe!

Cool or what?

*Rosalyne Lievesley (9)*
*Elston All Saints Primary School*


## A MOUTHFUL OF MAGGOTS

A tinful of tigers,
A basketful of ladders,
A mouthful of maggots,
A bowlful of black adders.

A cupful of cows,
A stampede of ants,
A bunch of belly dancers,
A houseful of pants.

*Samantha Bunting (11)*
*Forest Town Primary School*

## 'TICKER'

Cushion-ripper,
Lazy-kipper,
Little-barker,
Claw-marker,
Kitten-scarer,
Curtain-tearer,
Tail-wagger,
Slipper-dragger,
Play-fighter,
Bone-biter,
Sloppy-licker,
Ear-flicker
My young puppy, Ticker.

*Kaylie Jane Sessford & Holly Bolus  (9)*
*Forest Town Primary School*


## BIKE

Broke squeder
Good wheeler
Noise maker
Sharp braker
Wheel skidder
Bike consider
Bone shaker
Pedal maker
Suspension bouncer
Light pouncer
Slicker peeler
Gap sealer

*Jamie Humphries  (10)*
*Forest Town Primary School*

## THE LION!

Animal-predator,
Mad-editor,
Claw-catcher,
Meat-snatcher,
Mane-fluffer,
Getting-tougher,
Jaw-clatter,
Gets-fatter,
Animal-eater,
Antelope-beater,
Cub-cuddler,
Baby-smotherer,
Violence-maker,
Meat-taker,
Rule-breaker,
Always-stronger,
Forever-longer,
Lion-tougher!

*Michelle Howell  (10)*
*Forest Town Primary School*


## JACK-IN-A-BOX

Child-thriller,
Fun-filler,
Box-shocker,
Toddler-flocker,
Music-springer,
Fun-singer,
Body-bouncer,
Clown-pouncer.
That's my Jack-in-a-box.

*Rebecca Fern Davis  (9)*
*Forest Town Primary School*

## A HATFUL OF PANTS

A bunch of words
A faceful of ants
A carful of water
A hatful of pants

A bullfarm of fairies
A scrumcap of nymphs
A houseful of wild dogs
A tower of imps

A tractorful of snakes
A lorryload of hairs
A pondful of cars
A bookful of squares

*Kirsten Pendlebury  (10)*
*Forest Town Primary School*

## JACK-IN-A-BOX

Child-thriller,
Fun-filler,
Box-shocker,
Toddler-flocker,
Music-springer,
Fun-singer,
Body-bouncer,
Clown-pouncer
That's my Jack-in-a-Box!

*Emily Andreou  (11)*
*Forest Town Primary School*

## A SOCKFUL OF SCORPIONS

A sockful of scorpions,
A kettleful of hairs.
A stampede of rabbits,
A bunchful of bears!

A bookful of spiders,
A glassful of pies.
A pocketful of lemonade,
A mouthful of flies!

A bagful of brains,
A headful of money.
A boxful of freckles,
A heartful of honey!

A shellful of baby teeth,
A brainful of flies.
A treeful of dogs,
A boxful of eyes.

*Sarah Jevons (10)*
*Forest Town Primary School*


## UP, UP AND AWAY

The enormous sun going around or world.
As bright as an orange.
And when it is getting dark,
The sun starts to fade,
And the moon begins to appear.

*Laura Frost (8)*
*Glapton Primary School*

## UP, UP AND AWAY!

Here's my plane ready to go,
All around the world.
Up through space, right past Mars,
Whizzing around curl after curl.

To orbit the earth,
Is to be like the sun,
Going round and round,
Turning morn into dawn.

Here's the stars,
The moon as well,
The moon is much bigger than it looks from down below,
Asteroids flying and coming my way,
I'd better go back and find the right way!

*Gemma Allsop  (10)*
*Glapton Primary School*

## UP, UP AND AWAY

A rocket zooming through space
With all the stars falling down
Mars is not too far to see
The light at night so red, yellow, blue and black
It is so beautiful.
You can see all the world is just like a blue, green ball.

*Darren Bullock  (8)*
*Glapton Primary School*

## UP, UP, AND AWAY

A floating rocket flying gracefully
Aeroplane flying swiftly
Plant Mars floating swiftly.
Beautiful ice flying swiftly.
Lovely Earth floating slowly.
A floating aeroplane flying slowly.
A house clock clicking.
A floating planet flies in the sky.
A floating rocket flies gracefully.

*Wade Smith (8)*
*Glapton Primary School*




## UP, UP AND AWAY

A red rocket shooting past the stars
A blackbird flying through the sky
A fire is blazing away
A big sun shines on me
At night the stars twinkle on me
I watch the planes go by
At night the sky has a big moon
In the morning I watch the sun come up

*Daniel O'Gelsby (8)*
*Glapton Primary School*

## UP, UP AND AWAY

A floating aeroplane has a wing,
As the pilot starts to sing.
A floating rocket flying gracefully,
As planet Mars is floating swiftly.
Beautiful ice flying swiftly,
Lovely Earth floating slowly.

*David Hopkin  (8)*
*Glapton Primary School*


## UP, UP AND AWAY

A red and black jet plane
Zooming so fast you can't see it.
It goes flying through the stars.
As the jet goes past
A trail of wind comes towards us.

*Adam Hewitt  (7)*
*Glapton Primary School*


## UP, UP AND AWAY

Birds flying everywhere
Landing on people's lawns
Pecking at the bread
Flying off with it back to their homes
Feeding to the babies
Babies wanted it really quick

*Laura McKechnie  (11)*
*Glapton Primary School*

## UP, UP AND AWAY

A little cloud slowly moves
A little helicopter moves past a cloud
A small aeroplane flows past a star
A huge bird flies past the sky
A little blackbird moves a house
Up, up and down and way we go
We go up, up and up and away
Up and up and you go
It's good fun to be in the sky
On the way we go up in the sky

*Natasha Cope  (8)*
*Glapton Primary School*


## UP, UP AND AWAY

The big burning sun is throwing massive flames everywhere.
And when I see the shadows I run inside to hide
But then I get hot so I move to the shadow place.

*Kayleigh Desnos  (8)*
*Glapton Primary School*


## UP, UP AND AWAY

A floating planet flies in the sky
A floating rocket flies gracefully high
A star comes by and says goodbye
The moon shines on a cold winter's night.
Red Mars in the air
Then he says goodbye.

*James Freeman  (8)*
*Glapton Primary School*

## UP, UP AND AWAY

Up, down, round and round,
Look the loop, whizz round and down
The plane is fast until at last it stops
And stars all over again.

Chopping off the tops of trees,
I see black smoke coming out the back
Heading for a bright corner
Just made it round the corner.

What goes up must come down
Tries to reach the stars
But falls back before it gets there
And loops the loop again.

Up, down, round, down and whizz round corner
Round and down to people and places
Putt . . . putt . . . putt . . . to the pit stop
For it is out of fuel.

*Alice Foster (9)*
*Glapton Primary School*


## UP, UP AND AWAY

A red and black jet plane
Zooming so fast you can't see it.
It goes flying through the stars.
As the jet goes past
There's a trail of wind coming towards us.

*Aiden Clarke (8)*
*Glapton Primary School*

# THE DOLPHIN

She swims through the ocean,
As though she's put on a potion.

She sees the octopuses brushing their curls,
But she ignores them and carries on with her swirls.

She passes the whales,
And watches ships set sail.

She swims around the coral reef,
And sees marine fish swim beneath.

As you may have guessed by now,
She's an animal with a fin.

She can't be a pig, a sheep or cow,
But a *dolphin!*

*Hannah Senior (9)*
*Highfields School*


## MY MAGIC BOX

I would put a ticket to miss school,
A cleverness potion, I'm not a fool,
I would put wads of food,
A snazzy coat to look a dude,
And loads of drink,
Stink bombs to make a stink.

I would put the sounds of eating,
I would put chatting at a meeting,
I would put the sounds of cheering,
But not unhappy jeering.

*Matthew Willson (10)*
*Highfields School*

# THE WHALE

The large blue animal is called a whale,
Squirting water, swishing its tail.
The friendly giant, calm as can be,
He catches fish for lunch and tea.
He drifts along the ocean floor,
There's many places to explore.
The seaweed's waving to and fro,
He cruises around very slow.
He's as big as six elephants put together,
It's a pity he's not a bit more clever.
Or he would have caught lots more fish,
And then he would have a tastier dish.
I'd love to watch this wonderful creature,
If I saw one I could tell my teacher!

*Lizzie Simmonds  (9)*
*Highfields School*


## THE CROCODILE

No head, scales and
Water. Slithering and
Sliding swiftly through
The water like a torpedo.
Then waiting and waiting
Like a stone on a seabed.

The slightest move and it's
Off, like a rocket, thundering
Through the sky; leaving
Just peace and quiet.

*Freddie Reid  (11)*
*Highfields School*

## HEDGEHOG'S AUTUMN SONG

'Me, I'm cute
With my whiskery face
And my shambly shuffle.
I love you, Autumn.
You and your abundance
Of grubs and worms and slugs.
I'm feeling dozy, and you send down leaves
For my bed.
At night when I go out
To find my grub
I creep around slowly
And when I got back to my den
I am unharmed (apart from indigestion!)'

*Stephanie Derbyshire  (9)*
*Highfields School*


## TEACHER'S DESK

Do you know how many things
Your teacher can cram on her desk?
A hamster, a rat or something like that.
A computer, a Hoover van,
A frying pan,
An ancient mug of tea,
A ring of rusty keys,
A bowl of cold noodles from '93,
But I think by far the best thing is . . .

*Ciera Lovelock  (9), Katerina McCourt  (10),*
*Colette Ayers  (9), Tamsin Slade  (9)*
*Jesse Gray Primary School*

## PRINCESS STELLA

Once upon a time,
In a land so fair,
A princess called Stella,
Was brushing her hair.

'I'm fed up with these golden tresses,
I'm sick of all these fancy dresses,
What I need is something cool,
To make me really fit to rule.'

To the royal stylist Stella went,
She explained in detail her intent.
When she emerged her locks were green,
Pink and blue and aquamarine.

Her trousers were baggy,
Her T-shirt was tight,
And even her trainers,
Were made by Nike!

Everyone began to stare,
But transformed Stella,
Did not care.

In spite of all her subjects' laughter,
Our princess lived happily ever after.

*Hanah Tindle  (10)*
*Jesse Gray Primary School*

## THE INVISIBLE FRIEND

My sister has an invisible friend,
*Who I say isn't there,*
My sister has an invisible friend,
*Who plays with her every day.*

My sister has an invisible friend,
*Who never goes away,*
My sister has an invisible friend,
*It looks like she's talking to no one.*

My sister has an invisible friend,
*Who I say isn't there,*
My sister has an invisible friend,
*It's the only friend she's got!*

**Hanisha Sethi (10)**
**Jesse Gray Primary School**


## THE TELEPHONE BILL

When my mummy showed me the telephone bill,
It made me gasp, it sent a chill.
£2000 it said on the letter,
'You'd better stop, I mean you'd better.'
I haven't touched the phone for days,
I really will amend my ways.
But I can't keep my hand off the phone,
It's like a dog chewing its bone!
The telephone bill, well it was pretty long,
But I still can't see why Mum smacked my bum!

**Fay Masters & Anna Thwaites (10)**
**Jesse Gray Primary School**

# MY LIKES AND DISLIKES

Likes and dislikes
I like the cool breeze on a hot summer's day,
but not the chill of a very cold winter blast.
I like my hamster, all cute and grey,
but not the dirty rat that scurries so fast.

Likes and dislikes
I like playing tennis, hitting the ball with spin,
but not football because I'm not excellent.
I like listening to music and making a din,
but I don't really like being silent.

Likes and dislikes
I like eating, especially peppers, plums and chips,
but not olives, anchovies or green beans.
I like wearing tracksuits, T-shirts and tops,
but not anything tight like jeans.

*Ross Farrar (10)*
*Jesse Gray Primary School*

# SCHOOL

S uperb
C lever in every way
H elpful every day
O rganised
O pportunity
L earning

*Laura-Jane Barker (9)*
*Jesse Gray Primary School*

## WEATHER

Cold, windy, frosty,
Cars driving slowly,
Among the icy roads.
People walking to places,
Through the rain and the thunder,
Getting soaking wet.
As they get there,
They're dripping water everywhere,
As they trail in.
People get on to the bus,
Or get into a taxi,
As it starts to snow and hail.
You see children wrapped up warm,
In their woolly hats and scarves,
Mittens and wellingtons.
Dogs and cats,
Curled up indoors,
Lying next to the fire.
Squirrels and rabbits hibernating.
As it gets near to the end of winter,
You think it's nearly summer,
Then one day . . .
It's true,
The sun is here!

*Radhika Monisha Kalra  (10)*
*Jesse Gray Primary School*

# MY LIFE AS A LEAF

I start my life in the spring
as a tiny bud
on a gigantic tree.
Around me are my relatives
and the beautiful pink and white blossom,
floating down like sycamore.
I am silent, though eager
to tell them what I think of being a leaf.

The summer comes, with it the sunshine.
I see the merry hikers walking down below.
The rain and I are acquainted,
as the drops fall on my stem.
I find my body is wet.
But the wind comes and throws me around,
the drops fall onto the grass below.

Then comes autumn.
I turn red and gold
as the gentle wind Zephyrs
makes my relatives flutter to the ground.
I know I will die soon.
My life has been lazy
hanging on a tree all day.
I have a sinking feeling,
as I see my relatives being trampled on
I know I am next
as I flutter to the ground.
Dead.

*Katherine Stewart  (10)*
*Jesse Gray Primary School*

# WORDS ARE...

Passwords always play 'Guess who?',
Buying words want everything new.
Short words stand on all the other books,
Sly words care about their good looks.
Foreign words shrug and walk away,
Cheeky words backchat at everything you say.
Long words stand as tall as a flying bird,
Shy words hide behind every other word.
Thinking words make your thoughts go ting,
Loud words boast about every little thing.
Naughty words say no and never,
Boring words go on forever.
Swear words laugh in people's faces.
Quiet words sit and read in tiny spaces.
Careful words go out to play,
Clumsy words trip up on the way.
Loving words hold crimson roses,
Pretty words do their little poses.
Scary words shout *boo!*
Naughty words make fun of you.
You can find words in every book,
So why don't you take a look?

*Eleanor Barratt (10)*
*Jesse Gray Primary School*

## FIREWORKS

Waiting in my box,
Waiting to be free,
People get excited,
I hear them screaming outside,
Then I hear someone,
Creeping towards my box,
They pick me up,
I know what I have to do,
Just stay calm,
Put on the show of my life.

I am planted in my pot,
They light me,
I get ready,
Up I go scattering my colours,
Screaming,
Popping,
Up I go in the sky,
I use my red,
My orange, my green and my blue.
I leave my best for last,
My creamy white,
Everyone goes 'Wow',
Then I fall down,
Down, down, down.

I lie down burnt,
I know I have done my duty,
I feel proud of myself,
I hope my children will do as well.

*Fred Brewin  (10)*
*Jesse Gray Primary School*

## THE LEAVES

The leaves that fall on Sunday
   just
      trickle
      down
        on the hay.
The leaves that fall on Monday
twirl around all day.
The leaves that fall on Tuesday
just dribble down to doomsday.
The leaves that fall on Wednesday
just waddle down for washday.
The leaves that fall on Thursday
just sweep down for Friday.
The leaves that fall on Friday
just fall right down upon your head.
The leaves that fall on Saturday
just lie around all day.

*Rebecca Wallis (9)*
*Jesse Gray Primary School*


## BIN

Bubblegum 5 weeks old
Bread covered in mould
A shuttlecock, a medicine bottle
Tony's dead peat Axolotl
A Twix wrapper, a fly swatter
Some old trainers, a used plaster
And a tie worn by my headmaster.

A remote controlled car which had a crash
An old T-shirt from a 60s bash
A record player which made a din
And an old sponge cake in a silver tin.
A bullet which had been fired
And a tape which made you tired.
Why did they throw all this away?

*James Marsh  (10)*
*Jesse Gray Primary School*


## QUEEN LIZ RULES OK

I am Elizabeth,
I am queen.
This is my kingdom,
Where I reign supreme.
I'm Britain's beauty,
My words are the law.
All must obey me,
The rich and the poor.
My clothes are encrusted,
With jewels so rare.
I'm covered in gold,
From my toes to my hair.
I am Elizabeth,
And now you must say.
Whatever happens,
Queen Liz rules OK!

*Sarah Hudson  (10)*
*Jesse Gray Primary School*

## ONE DAY . . .

One day I will sail all the oceans to fulfil my heart's desires,
One day I will invent something that no one else has ever invented,
One day I will watch the dolphins swim in Dingle Bay,
One day I will help other people who are not as lucky as me,
One day I will dance upon a stage like Darcie Bussell,
One day I will look back on my life and realise how fortunate I have
    been.

*Beth Lacey  (10)*
*Jesse Gray Primary School*


## AUNTY MARY

Aunty Mary is rather hairy,
She picks her nose,
And sucks her toes,
She bites her nails,
And crunches snails.
*So beware!*
My Aunty Mary is rather scary.

*Heidi Ford  (9)*
*Jesse Gray Primary School*


## MONSTERS

Have you ever seen an alien from space?
Have you ever seen a cyclops's face?
Have you ever seen a zombie cry?
Have you ever seen a vampire fly?
Have you ever seen a werewolf at night?
Have you ever seen a dragon fight?
I haven't, have you?

*Gracie Kildare  (9)*
*Jesse Gray Primary School*

## A Winter's Night

It was cold and gloomy that night,
I stood there watching the stars glisten,
There were snowflakes falling from the heavens above,
I was frozen and had frostbite,
There were icicles hanging from every rooftop.
Suddenly a clump of snow fell from behind me,
There was white everywhere,
I was lost in a sea of confusion and despair.

It was cold and gloomy that night,
There were snowmen melting in the school playground,
Voices echoing in the night sky
And screams lost from the morning before.
Suddenly a hand clutched my shoulder, aagghhrr,
I disappeared into the mist slowly, slowly sinking!

*Hannah Percival  (10)*
*Jesse Gray Primary School*

## Recipe For Winter

Sprinkle some snow and here we go
Dash some slush on roads squelching as the cars go by
Whisk some chilly howling winds dashing through the trees
Add some sparkling frost and sprinkle on the cold ground
Pour some delighted children throwing snowballs
Stir some children sliding on the ice
Decorate with a cheerful robin sitting on a one side
And you have made winter!

*Lewis Williams  (8)*
*Keyworth Primary School*

## TIME

Sand trickling through
Second by second,
Minute by minute,
Hour by hour,
Day by day,
Week by week,
Month by month,
Time year by year,
Century by century,
Millennium by millennium,
Decade by decade,
Time never ending,
Grains of sand always trickling through.

*Sam Costall  (10)*
*Keyworth Primary School*


## BUTTERFLY

B   eautiful butterfly
U   nder a flower
T   wisting, fluttering and
T   urning around
E   verywhere you go
R   eds and blues, yellows and greens
F   ascinating colours, wherever you can be seen
L   ying and flying
Y   ou go, gardens and meadows
    So peacefully you go by

*Naomi Jameson  (9)*
*Keyworth Primary School*

## RECIPE FOR WINTER

Take some sparkling ice
and sprinkle it all over the roads
Whisk in some chilly north wind
and make it whirl around
Pour some fluttering flakes
to glisten in the snow
Add in the lashing rain
spluttering all over cars
Shake some slushy sleet
through the howling wind
Decorate with merry children
throwing glistening snowballs
And you have made winter!

*Rebecca Blackburn  (7)*
*Keyworth Primary School*

## CHRISTMAS

C   hristmas carols sung on Christmas morning
H   olly decorates our homes
R   udolph has a shiny nose
I    like Santa
S   anta delivers presents
T   o our house
M   anger where they lay Jesus
A   ngels in the sky
S   tars shine brightly and strong

*Symon Akinin  (8)*
*Keyworth Primary School*

## CHRISTMAS

C hristmas is for cards colourful and bright
H is holly red ripe berries
R is Rudolph with shiny nose
I is the innkeeper who was ever so generous
S for the stable where Jesus was born
T is for toys from Santa
M is for Mary mother of Jesus
A is for the angel's good song
S is for the sign that Jesus is alive

*Samantha Collard (8)*
*Keyworth Primary School*

## TOYS

What am I able to do with my mind?
Play with my dolls and make sure I am kind?
Will I play tea parties or with my dolls?
Or will I be scared of my magical trolls?

*Grace Shields (11)*
*Keyworth Primary School*

## CHRISTMAS

C hristmas crackers being cracked.
H elping others to celebrate Christmas.
R udolph who helps Santa.
I nnkeeper who was so kind.
S anta's helpers who bring joy to children.
T rees are being put up to light the world.

*Peter Frame (7)*
*Keyworth Primary School*

## MY DOG

With floppy ears and a cold wet nose,
My little dog has scratchy toes,
Catching his ball or sniffing a snail,
Running around and chasing his tail.

A sloppy tongue licking my face,
Going for walks, or running a race,
Chewing his bone, snoozing all day,
Playing together come what may.

Barking at noises and tickling my feet,
Sharing my toys and eating a sweet,
The best of friends it's plain to see,
That I love him and he loves me.

*Tiffany Sisson  (9)*
*Keyworth Primary School*


## CHRISTMAS

C   for carols being sung
H   for holly decorating the house
R   for Rudolph flying through the sky
I    for innkeeper who gave them rest
S   for the stable where Jesus was born
T   for the toys Santa has brought
M   for Mary rocking the manger
A   for angels fluttering around
S   o here we are celebrating his birth

*Amber Whittaker  (7)*
*Keyworth Primary School*

## THE DESERTED COTTAGE

There's no smoke in the chimney,
And the rain beats on the floor,
There's no glass in the windows,
There's no wood in the door,
The heather grows behind the house,
And the sand lies before,
No hand has trained the ivy,
The walls are grey and bare,
The boats upon the sea sail by,
Nor even go there,
No beast of the field comes near,
Nor any bird of the air,
But in the quiet dusk a discerning eye,
Might see a lonely figure there,
Fluttering through the deserted cottage,
Savouring the memories lingering clear.

*Tara Elston  (10)*
*Keyworth Primary School*


## CHRISTMAS

C   andles are lit in the town square.
H   olly is on every person's door.
R   ide on Rudolph the red-nosed reindeer.
I    sit in front of the fire to keep warm when it is very cold.
S   itting waiting all the Christmas night.
T   oast for breakfast, Christmas Day it is!
M   y mum opens the door so we can open our presents.
A   Game Boy, a telescope, everything I wanted.
S   o enjoy your Christmas too!

*Michael Cox  (7)*
*Keyworth Primary School*

## THE MOUSE

Walking through the grass one day
I came across a mouse
I picked it up and stroked it
And asked, 'Where is your house?'

It jumped off my hand
And then ran to a tree,
The next time I saw it
It was sitting at the side of me.

I asked, 'Are you hungry?
In my pocket I have some cheese.'
The mouse looked very excited
And nodded and said, 'Yes, please.'

*Matthew Webster (10)*
*Keyworth Primary School*


## CHRISTMAS

C   is for candles lit to light up the house
H   is for holly, making happy homes
R   is for Rudolph going over rooftops
I    is for people staying indoors
S   is for snow falling everywhere
T   is for toys, children enjoying them
M  is for Mary, baby's mother
A   is for Angels singing loud and clear
S   is for Santa on his sleight

*Leah Fielding (7)*
*Keyworth Primary School*

## Down Under

The water was a clear blue, so inviting to the dry world.
I am sorry to say I was beckoned,
The tide was calling me.
I jumped, as I hit the water I felt the feeling,
The feeling of cool refreshing water.
Deeper, deeper,
I was urged down, down into the undiscovered depths.
I saw things I had only dreamt about.
Things that existed only in fairy tales.
Barnacles surrounded me clinging onto the rocks.
I felt I was part of this magical underwater wonder.
My air was going, I had to go.
*No! No!*
This world is my heaven,
I want to stay here.
It was screaming inside my head.
I was leaving that place where I thought I belonged.
I hit the top of the water *splash!*
My best adventure ever!

*Laura Blackburn (11)*
*Keyworth Primary School*


## Toys

What are you able to do with your toys?
Jumping and bouncing with girls and boys
Will you build palaces, castles or towers?
Will you use boxes or your magical powers?
Will I play horses or my dolls?
Or go in the garden and play with my trolls?
Will I play on my slide or on the swings?
Or will I play with boxes and things?

*Stephanie Collard (11)*
*Keyworth Primary School*

## LADY LOVE SNOBWORTH

Lady Love Snobworth Mash Bellworth Sneeze
Was indulging herself with a plateful of cheese.

When the shutters flew open and her plate fell and broke
And the room filled up with some ghastly black smoke.

The Lady Love Snobworth exclaimed with a wheeze
All this thick fog is making me sneeze!

Then up from the kitchen there came such a din
That Lady Love Snobworth jumped out of her skin.

The moaning, the groaning, the crashes and slashes
Was followed by the sound of Snobworth's new glasses.

They tumbled and rumbled and fell down the stairs
And poor old Miss Snobworth was caught unawares.

She screamed aloud, screamed and fainted just there
She hit her head hard but was too scared to care.

She picked up her Vodka and got out a glass
And all the loud noises were gone in a flash!

*Helen Cox (10)*
*Keyworth Primary School*


## CANDLE

The flame dances like a little man, hopping from foot to foot.
As the wax drips it makes a rock face,
The flame shines blue, red and yellow,
As it flickers it reminds me of the setting sun as it fades then disappears.

*Sarah Blatherwick (9)*
*Keyworth Primary School*

## A JOURNEY BY TRAIN

It went past in a cloud of smoke,
It was so dehydrating it made me choke.
Making noise as she approaches,
Dragging behind her were her coaches.
Towards Scotland she descends,
Turning lots of corners and lots of bends.
Passing fields full of corn,
Then I saw a man mowing his lawn.
Slowly but surely we reached the station,
And when I got off I reserved an invitation.

*Naomi Frame  (11)*
*Keyworth Primary School*


## THE LAST PETAL OF A ROSE

All the petals had fallen
Apart from this one
Although it had withered
Still it fought on
Through frost and snow
Until spring was upon
Yet still it fought on.

*Hollie Doughty  (10)*
*Keyworth Primary School*


## MY TWO NAUGHTY PETS

I have a naughty cat,
She's a bit of a brat.
She chews on my slippers,
So no more fat kippers.

I have a bad rabbit,
With a very bad habit.
He kicks and scratches and more,
So I shut his hutch door.

*Aisha Kay Michael (11)*
*Keyworth Primary School*

## SCHOOL

School is boring, but sometime's *fun,*
the teacher's coming, let's all run.

After break we have music, let's all sing along,
do you know a song?

Dinners are nice, so are puddings,
*Hooray* for chocolate puddings.

But can you guess my favourite time,
the time that I like best of all?

It's *home time.*

*Grant Allen (8)*
*King Edwin Primary School*

## WINTER

Inside the bitter blanket a ball of life,
Inside the ball of life a frozen waterfall,
Inside the frozen waterfall cold white snowflake,
Inside the cold white snowflake the north star,
Inside the north star the winter's eye,
Inside the winter's eye the bitter blanket.

*Jacomo Nardi-Forster (8)*
*King Edwin Primary School*

## KITTEN

She needs
Bouncing back legs to help her pounce on her pride
A tongue that feels like fine sandpaper in her smooth soft mouth
Ears that prick up and pinpoint particular sounds
Whiskers that twitch to feel the atmosphere
A tail that swishes and twitches to and fro
Fur that you can run you fingers down very softly
Claws that scratch and scrape your skin
Teeth so sharp they can chomp, chew and crunch their food

*Michaela Reeve  (9)*
*King Edwin Primary School*


## THE FISH

I saw
A scaly fish
Swimming through the ocean
Playing with the bigger fish
Consumed.

*Nikki Thomas  (10)*
*King Edwin Primary School*


## MOLE

He needs
A black body like a dark ebony tunnel,
Four huge feet like mini diggers to burrow through the dirty earth,
A pair of tiny slit eyes like two specks of coal,
A long thin snout with a tiny pink nose on the end like a bead to sniff
A set of small and sharp teeth to chomp his feast of worms,
Last but not least a pair of tiny ears to pinpoint every sound

*Amber Lyons (9) & Rebecca Rodgers  (10)*
*King Edwin Primary School*

## I WOULD RATHER BE

I would rather be A than Z
I would rather be a teacher than a head.
I would rather eat cake than bread.
I would rather a plague went away than spread.
I would rather use wool than thread.
I would rather be followed than led.
I would rather buy gold than heavy lead.
I would rather have a house than a shed.
I would rather feed than be fed.
I would rather fly than tread.
I would rather have shouted than said.
I would rather be up than in bed.
I would rather be skin-coloured than sunburnt red.
I would rather she stayed than fled.
I would rather cut than shred.

*Caroline Foster (11)*
*King Edwin Primary School*

## BUDGIE

A loud cheeper.
A big cage.
A bell ringer.
A lovely singer.
A round beak.
A high flyer . . .
. . . A budgie.

*James Peacock (9)*
*King Edwin Primary School*

# I WOULD LIKE TO . . .

I would like to taste the wind in the moonlit air.
    I should like to paint a twittering of a small bird sitting in a tree.
I would like to hear the passing of the millennium on the
                            highest peak of a mountain.
    I should like to taste a summer's sunset and feel the
                            warmth of the rising moon.
I would like to tie a knot in the rainbow, above the clouds high.
    I should like to discover unfound secrets of the mysterious oceans.
I would like to see the moon, instead of the sun, in the sky at noon,
    and for the sun to light the night sky and live with the stars.

*Hannah Peacock  (11)*
*King Edwin Primary School*


# UP, UP AND AWAY

My kite pulls me,
As if to say,
'Set me free,
Let me dance in the blue sky,
Dodge in and out
Of the candy floss clouds.
Let me sail through the heavens!
Let the wind take me,
Up, up and away.'

*Katie Holmes  (9)*
*King Edwin Primary School*


# A SONG TO SING

I can sing a song to you,
But only if you want me to.

I can sing a song that's true,
A song about me and you.

I like to sing about the bees,
And the wind blowing in the trees.

I like to sing most of all,
When we're all sitting in our school hall.

*Charlotte Saunders (7)*
*King Edwin Primary School*


# PIG

She needs
Skin like sand scattered on a beach,
A nose like a pink plate, stuck in the middle of her face,
A troublesome tail, twisting into the distance.
Ears like everlasting electric towers,
Feet like faint frantic black blobs, skipping slowly away.
She sounds like my dad when he snores.

*Sarah Moore & Pia Jackson (9)*
*King Edwin Primary School*


# THE UNICORN

The star of frost and snow sparkled over the unicorn
That danced in the moonlight,
That pranced in the moonlight,
And shone like a penny in the moonlight.
And the wave of its hair like a storm
And the sparkle in its eye
And the moonbeam shone on its back like glitter
And the black sky next to the unicorn's eye.

*Lucie Moore (7)*
*King Edwin Primary School*

## I SHOULD LIKE TO . . .

I should like to touch a twinkling star that shines in the night sky.
I should like to keep a warm sun ray in a jar,
So I could still have light at night.
I would like to taste the cheese of the moon.
I would like to swim in every ocean the Earth holds.

I should like to count every grain of sand on every beach.
To see every wild animal in Africa.
To go back in time to see the first living thing.
I should like to see the glow of the glow-worms in the
                                        middle of the night.
Or the sparkle of green eyes from cats hidden away.

*Rachel Pearson  (11)*
*King Edwin Primary School*

## WISHES

I would like to help birds fly in the summer if it has hurt its wing,
I would like to hold the stars and bring them down to earth,
I would like to hang the moon in my own bedroom so I can see it glow
        in the dark,
I would like to go up to heaven and bring some angels down to earth,
I would like to feel Jupiter and its ring without breaking it,
I would like to count every star in space every night,
I would like to go in the ocean and play with the dolphins,
I would like to eat all the fish in the ocean because I like every kind of
        fish, but only the little fish.

*Jodi Thomas  (9)*
*King Edwin Primary School*

## AFRICAN ELEPHANT

He needs
A trunk like turning and twisting telephone tubes,
Ears like elite, elegant flags, and tusks, the soft colour of ivory and
milky white
Feet like colossal fireplaces storming through.
Skin like baked, wrinkled clay in the roasting sun,
Tail, small and stiff, as heavy as a feathered hat,
His habit of snorting heavily, horribly.
His eating with his long trunk, ripping branches off trees,
And finally, his drinking, slurping from the slow moving stream.

*Zack Whittaker  (11)*
*King Edwin Primary School*

## WILD RABBIT

She will need . . .
Bounding feet for burrowing deep into the underworld.
A cautious wet nose for scenting cabbage, carrots and lettuce,
And powerful hind legs to push her up into the atmosphere.
Her ears prick up like porcupines' spines, at the drop of a pin.
Her bright red eyes shine like traffic lights, glowing in the gloomy dark
nights.
Her bobbing, furry snowball tail twitches at her every move.
And her tiny unseen mouth holds razor sharp dragon's teeth of steel.
A wild but cuddly pet.

*Charlotte Mendham  (10) & Alexandra J Peck  (9)*
*King Edwin Primary School*

## WHALE

He needs
A body like an everlasting oval.
Teeth like the bristles of a brush.
Fins like the flapping wings of a bird.
His mouth like a secret door.
As his noble head swims through the ocean the krill drift into his
mouth.
They go into the stomach of the sea.

*James de Gilbert (11)*
*King Edwin Primary School*


## UP, UP AND AWAY

I ride on the cloud
floating in the air
feeling the thrashing wind in my face
floating up, up and away.

*Scott Bonser (9)*
*King Edwin Primary School*


## LITTLE HELICOPTER

High and high in the sky.
Little helicopter may fly.
Reddish blue and green too.
Twinkles, sparkles in the air.
So high, so high in the sky.
Up, up and away!

*Gemma Key (7)*
*King Edwin Primary School*

## SWIMMING POOL

Splish splash
Drip drop
'Whee'
*Plop!*
Whoosh whizz
Bang, bump
Yelling shouting
Laughing screaming
Splish splash
Drip drop
'Whee'
*Plop!*
Chit chat
Slip slide
Thin wide
Hush humm
Splish splash
Drip drop
'Whee'
*Plop!*

*Katie Worker (10)*
*Peafield Lane Primary & Junior School*


## THE COOL PENGUIN

There was a cool penguin on ice,
Who thought that ice skating was nice,
He said one cold day,
I'll skate right away,
Then he did and flipped over twice!

*Bethany-May Bramley (11)*
*Peafield Lane Primary & Junior School*

## THERE WAS A YOUNG GIRL FROM BOMBAY

There was a young girl from Bombay,
Who took her driving test one day,
    The examiner got out,
    With a heck of a shout,
'You fool, you're going the wrong way.'

*Hazel Fletcher (10)*
*Peafield Lane Primary & Junior School*


## HEDGEHOG

Round spiky hedgehog
Does not make a single sound
On a cold dark night.

*Philippa Stevens (10)*
*Peafield Lane Primary & Junior School*


## THE MAN FROM THE SKY

There was a man from high in the sky
On his descent he said, 'Bye, bye!'
He aimed for a spot
A painted white dot
He thought he was going to die.

*Joseph Tozer (10)*
*Peafield Lane Primary & Junior School*

## THE . . .

The . . .
Soft fur
Not a word
Flaming eyes
So wise
Sneaking
Peeking
Peeking
Sneaking
Two eyes
Little tears
Eating mice
So nice.

*Samuel Johnson  (10)*
*Peafield Lane Primary & Junior School*


## WINTER

Winter is an old man's face,
White and weary,
Cold and teary,
Sitting down on the ground.
Too afraid to make a sound,
First he's there, then he's gone,
First there's some, then there's none.

Winter is an old man's face,
Fading away,
Nothing to say.

*Emma Clifford  (11)*
*Peafield Lane Primary & Junior School*

## RECIPE FOR A GOOD HARVEST

Take some rosy red apples,
And crunchy leaves,
Add some rain and whipped clouds,
Some sunshine, some breeze,
Then go out onto the diamond grass,
And pick up some silk conkers,
Sprinkle on some golden trees,
Along with some juicy fruit and veg.
Round it off with some apple pie,
And wrap it up with the milkman's song.

*Michelle Sayer  (11)*
*Peafield Lane Primary & Junior School*


## LIZARD

L   ittle creatures,
I   guanas big,
Z   igzag patterns on their back,
A   nd all the colours of the rainbow,
R   unaway bigger animals,
D   eep in the trees I hide

*Thomas Price  (9)*
*Peafield Lane Primary & Junior School*


## THE FOX HUNT

Rushing through the grass.
Dogs were racing past.
The fox's heart was beating like a drum.
The sound of the barking came closer.
The fox raced into the distance.
She didn't return until the hunt had finished.

The hunt was on.
And the fox stood its ground.
The dog from the pack was just about to pounce.
The fox ran out of sight.
The dogs were racing after the fox.
The fox was out of breath.
As the fox met her death.

*Katie Terry  (10)*
*St Joseph's RC Primary School*


## MATHS TEST

The teacher walks in
Chucks her rubbish in the bin
She shouts, 'We're having a test.'
The number freak says, 'Yes!
Maths tests are just the best.'

He is the teacher's pet
He'll get ten out of ten I would bet
He's the teacher's helper for a week
We think he's a creep and a number freak.

I'm on the last sum
People think that I'm dumb
That was our last test
The number freak says, 'Yes!
Maths tests are the best.'

*Joseph Ward  (10)*
*St Joseph's RC Primary School*

## IMAGINATION

I ran from a lion with his mouth open wide
I jumped in the bushes to find a place to hide
I saw a pond in the distance
I ran and jumped in
The lion ran right past me and crashed into a bin
I could hold my breath no longer, I crept out of the pond
The huge bin behind me held a magic wand
The bin's thin green arm waved the wand in my direction
I ran behind a giant turtle for my own protection
The turtle turned to a velvet dragon that breathed orange flames
The dragon slapped me with his tail into some rusty mirror frames
The mirror frames quickly grew legs and kicked me far away
I landed on a treasure island and stayed there for the day.

*Joe Foster  (10)*
*St Joseph's RC Primary School*


## OH NO, A MATHS TEST

The teachers said, 'Books out for a maths test.'
Oh no, a maths test today,
My brain has gone as blank as a window,
As Miss calls the numbers out just like at bingo.
My hands are shaking like money jingling,
People keep looking and staring at me,
Miss gave the last question,
A hard calculation,
57 x 22 = This is the one I can do.

*Natalie Proffitt  (10)*
*St Joseph's RC Primary School*

## MY CAT

When  my cat looks into the pond
He leaps back in surprise
He stares at the cat looking at him
And glares with his opened-wide eyes

When my cat sees another cat
He tries to pick a fight
He fights all day and never stops
Until he sees a mouse at first sight

When my cat is asleep
He is as quiet as a mouse
You can never hear him make a sound
In the bedroom of the house

*Lyndsey Davis  (11)*
*St Joseph's RC Primary School*


## I HAD A DREAM

I had a dream all wars had stopped
I had a dream all children fed
I had a dream the world was fair
I had a dream people would share.
I had a dream of mums and dads
And in that dream were happy kids.
I had a dream of schools for all
I had a dream of peace.

*Emily Bottomley  (11)*
*St Joseph's RC Primary School*

## THE SURPRISE MATHS TEST

We sat down and the teacher said, 'Surprise!'
We looked around, shivering as the test sheets arrived.
Worried faces, open mouths,
Eyes glanced down on the desks,
And frowns spread across the classroom
As the test began.

'First question . . .' the teacher said
And I was sure that she was mad.
I can't do a sum like that!
I scribbled down an answer that I knew was wrong.
This test is surely very long!
I was sweating and I was very hot,
But I would not give up.

Fourth question . . . Sixth question . . .
(Oh I need more time on that one!)
And the maths test ended
But please, I need my answers mended!
Our sheets got collected in
And the teacher smiled
As she went out.

*Kate Scotford  (10)*
*St Joseph's RC Primary School*


## THE DREAM

Through the night I dream about monsters
When I am fast asleep.
One night in my imagination I heard
The monster's voice, growling
Under the stairs.
So beware, you will be in for a scare.

His feet are like flippers flipping all the way.
His voice is croaky.
His fire is so smoky.
His scales are so rusty and dusty.
So beware, you will be in for a scare.
See him if you dare.

*Clare Bell*
*St Joseph's RC Primary School*


## THE DREADED MATHS TEST

The children sat shaking in their small brown chairs,
As the maths test papers were handed out with care,
Eyes stared around the classroom,
Mouths were gaping,
Sighs of horror spread around,
Panic and fear spread across everyone's face.

The test had just started, some children were crying,
As the teacher sat in her chair smiling,
Dean almost wet himself,
Julie was sweating buckets,
The others sat shaking as questions were asked.

Dean wasn't so worried, he knew all the answers,
Julie got through them alright,
The others tried their best of course,
Then -
The test was over,
The kids let out a sigh,
Now the marking begins, the results were all high,
We all passed with ten out of ten.

*Charlotte Appleby (11)*
*St Joseph's RC Primary School*

## OCEAN WAVES

Way, way out to sea
In a special place for fish to be
In a place no human eye can see
Lies a beautiful bed of coral.

The fish swim under the swelling tide
They dance and twist in a game of hide
Colours glistening, reflect in the sun
Harlequin patterns dance and run.

Shadows of a shipwreck hide
A treasure chest, once someone's pride
A wondrous place of everyone's dreams
This magical ocean, is more than it seems.

*Rebecca Rose  (10)*
*St Joseph's RC Primary School*


## DOLPHIN

Dolphin gliding through the sea
Come and glide to me
I shall be your friend
And your problems I shall mend
Tomorrow we shall swim together
Tomorrow we shall swim forever
Dolphin I saw you jump last night
Jump to the stars and bathe on the moon
Dolphin I heard you call last night
I heard you call for a friend ~
I shall be that friend
And your problems I shall mend.

*Stephanie Bostock  (11)*
*St Joseph's RC Primary School*

## THE SEA CAN...

The sea can be grumpy
The sea can be crazy
The sea can be rough
And is always tough.

The sea can yell
The sea can splash
The sea can tear
Because it hasn't a care.

The sea can be peaceful
The sea can be flat
The sea can be calm
And never do any harm.

The sea can sing
The sea can twist
The sea can glide
But never can hide.

The sea can roar
Up onto the shore
The sea can be warm
But not in a storm.

The sea can be great
It's just like a mate
The sea has waves
Which crash against caves.

*Melanie Ogilvie  (11)*
*St Joseph's RC Primary School*

## CYMRUS DRAGON

Dragon, dragon, magical
Beast
Perched on Snowdon bold
And strong.
Guard your land
With careful eyes.
Anyone who trespasses
Pays with their lives.

A knight from the east came
Galloping.
He rode a powerful
Stallion.
With armour, spear and sword.
To battle with the dragon
Of Cymrus.

He rode through rivers, fords
And lakes.
Galloped through forests and down
Country lanes.
And finally reaching the border of Wales,
He rode all the way to Snowdon.

Be careful, dragon, in your
Mountain realm.
He's coming with shield and with
Sword.
A battle to fight, a battle to
Win.
And a legend to make of your name.

*Kyle John Hope-Parry (11)*
*St Joseph's RC Primary School*

## PLAYGROUND BLUES

The left-hand side of the playground holds the scruffy mucky boys.
The right-hand side of the playground holds the clean and tidy girls.
The mucky boys play football with mud up to the knees,
While the clean girls write in diaries with their own kinky keys.
Julie forbids the girls to go onto the left
And Darren forbids the boys to go onto the right.
But Julie and Darren fall in love at first sight.
Julie now plays football on the left, red and flustered,
While the girls on the right write in diaries, quite disgusted.

*Elizabeth Upton  (11)*
*St Joseph's RC Primary School*


## CHEETAH

She runs like the wind so swiftly
She pounces from rocks and she jumps on her prey.
She hides her cubs in the grass
Then she kisses her cubs goodbye and off she goes to give a strike.
She comes back with a tasty bite
So they can eat all through the night.
They shone in the morning light
Off she goes again to try another strike.
Her cubs stay still like statues
While she goes running her way.
She bites an antelope on the legs
While the antelope begs and begs.
The antelope starts to kick
While the cheetah gave a lick.

*Michaela Key  (10)*
*St Joseph's RC Primary School*

## THE SHAKING MATHS TEST

I was shaking and so was my chair
Why do we do all these tests?
It's not fair!
My pencil was wobbling,
Like a jelly on a plate
Can I say I am sick,
Or is it too late?

He stood in the middle of the room
He said it was the maths test soon
He smiled a cold smile, and then he began
And pencils are scribbling to the sound of the man.

> 'Nine times nine
> (I did it in my head)

> Ninety add three hundred
> (I feel a bit hot now)

> Eleven times eight
> (I did my eleven times table)

> Eight add twelve
> (I counted on my fingers)

> Five times ten
> (Five, ten, fifteen)

We swapped over papers, my friend marked mine
She smiled as she passed it back to me . . .
I looked at my score . . .
It was ten out of ten!
Let's do it again!

*Joanna Law  (10)*
*St Joseph's RC Primary School*

## MY DOG ON BONFIRE NIGHT

In the house there lies a little dog.
His heart is beating rapidly.
Big bangs all around.
Make frightening sounds ~ on bonfire night.
He snuggles up and tries to hide.
And his wet nose is hidden from view.

When fireworks explode all quiet is ruined,
Why can't it just be calm?
Let the colour, the light and the patterns go on
But have silence instead of explosion.

*Syann Hall  (10)*
*St Joseph's RC Primary School*


## THE MATHS TEST

Everybody's trembling
Pens and pencils shaking
People are saying 'I can do it'
The teacher is coming with maths books.
The chatter stops
As the teachers says 'number 1'
Pens and pencils scribble the answer
People are still trembling
You can hear tick, tick, tick of the classroom clock.

*Stacie Leigh Daniels  (10)*
*St Joseph's RC Primary School*

## SCHOOL DINNERS

School dinners, school dinners,
Bits and bobs,
Meat from the oven, heat from the holes.

Chips are not greasy,
They are not hard,
They taste just right,
Not covered in lard.

School dinners, school dinners,
The pudding arrives,
Cookies with chocolate
~ A lovely surprise.

The topping is syrup,
A creative dish,
It's almost as good,
As a wonderful wish.

*Jadey Ola Eland (10)*
*St Joseph's RC Primary School*

## CHOCOLATE

Chocolate's brown, it's all in squares.
It's yummy scrummy nice to eat.
It's the world's perfect treat,
Cadburys, Rowntrees and Nestlé too,
It's a treat for me and you.
No more chips and no more crisps,
Have some chocolate, it's the best.

Nag your mum to buy you some.
Then offer her the smallest piece.
It's wrapped in silver foil and paper,
There's a chocolate maker out there now,
Churning chocolate by the hour,
Chocolate that anyone could devour,
Chocolate's not good for you but I like it.

*Louise Dawson  (11)*
*Saville House School*


## HOOVER MONSTER

Playing in the hallway
School is years away
Our mum starts the cleaning
It must be Wednesday.

The cupboard in the hallway
Opens to reveal
The Hoover monster lurking
We both let out a squeal!

Tall and green with bulging eyes
We need to move our toys
Sticky fingers in our ears
We must cut out the noise.

*Rachael Briggs  (10)*
*Saville House School*

## MY GARDEN

In the winter it is covered with a thick layer of snow.
Robins peck at the bird feeder trying to get some nuts.

In spring it is green.
My dad and I plant seeds.

In summer it is hot.
Sarah and I have a water fight.

In autumn the leaves are brown.
Squirrels collect nuts for the winter.

*Victoria Woodhead  (10)*
*Saville House School*


## UP, UP AND AWAY

Every night I see a star,
In the sky above,
I wish that I could fly so far,
Giving my heart some love.

My mum took me on an aeroplane,
On which I felt very ill,
Just then it went up even more,
So my mum gave me a pill.

We saw some birds,
That were very high,
I wish that I was a bird,
I wish that I could fly.

*Sheree Parry  (9)*
*Sherwood Junior School*

## UP, UP AND AWAY

Ever since I can remember I've been afraid of heights,
It makes me sick when I look below to see the sights.
I went in an aeroplane, I was sick on my dad,
I went in a helicopter, I was sick on my grandad.
It was my birthday,
I got a puppy called Kay,
I had a surprise,
I hoped it would be something I despise.
My mum took me for a hot-air balloon ride,
I shouted! I cried!
I looked into the skies.
This wasn't so bad.
I was happy *(not sad)*

**Michiela Robey (10)**
**Sherwood Junior School**

## UP, UP AND AWAY

I have always been afraid of heights,
The only thing I like about the sky, is flying kites
I once went in a hot-air balloon,
It felt like I was in a great big galloon.

Soon it was over and I was so, so glad,
My sister loved it and because it was over
She was so, so sad.

**Zoe Pickering (9)**
**Sherwood Junior School**

## UP, UP AND AWAY

Up, up and away in the sky,
I still can't believe I can fly!
I fly with the birds
Where I cannot be heard,
I'm glad I'm not scared of heights!

I was flying yesterday
When an aircraft came my way.
I shouted for help,
But it came full pelt
So I sped right out of its way!

Flying about is ace!
But myself, I need to brace.
It gave me a shock
When I walked off the docks
And hovered straight into the air!

*Mitchell Ryan  (10)*
*Sherwood Junior School*


## WHO RUNS THE SCHOOL ANYWAY?

Could it be Dr Tozer? Could it be NF?
Could it be Mrs Smith or could it be me?
It could be Mr Scully who handles all the tools,
Or BJ who kicks footballs.
If Dr Tozer was not at the school we would not have a pool,
If we did not have NF we would not have any Latin.
They all have their part of running the school
But I think the person who runs the rest of the school is me.
I swim in the pool
And use the things Mr Scully fixes with his tools.

*Niall Goldie  (9)*
*Wellow House School*

## WHO RUNS THIS SCHOOL ANYWAY?

Mr Bevell is a fool,
But sometimes he can be cool,
He is the head of music,
If he put a plug in a socket
He has got to be careful he does not fuse it.
So I do not think it is him.

Mr BS is going to be a dad,
But the baby will make him mad,
PBS has a long red nose,
He may trip over his own toes.
So I do not think it is him.

CK is very fun,
But at games he makes you run,
Sometimes he just forgets you're there.
So I do not think it is him.

Mrs BS is married to Mr BS,
They are husband and wife,
In our French lessons she is full of life.
She went to the hospital for her baby's scan,
When she got home she asked for the fan.
So I do not think it is her.

I think I know who runs the school,
But I will not say because I am no fool,
Actually I think I am quite cool.

*Megan Dolby  (10)*
*Wellow House School*

## WHO RUNS THIS SCHOOL ANYWAY?

Mr Scully is totally cool,
He climbs on roofs,
He fixes pipes,
He is head of tools.
He fixes desks,
Doors and heating,
And he takes a heck of a lot of beating.
He fixes tables for eating,
He makes blackboards,
And fixes our swimming pool,
Makes sure all is secure.
So it's pretty obvious Mr Scully runs the school,
You see,
He looks after you and me.

*Ashley Hopkinson (10)*
*Wellow House School*


## THE HAUNTED WOOD

The haunted wood taunts, so people say,
So people move gradually away.
As the wood grows larger and larger,
The people move faster and faster.
Eventually the town is deserted
And the wood is diverted onto another town,
To move them away
So the wood can prove
That it can stay
Upon the land where it wants to lay.

*Justin Byles (11)*
*Wellow House School*

## WHO RUNS THIS SCHOOL ANYWAY?

Mr BS is the head of English,
He lets us write about anything, like fish.
In the classroom he is fun,
But on the games field he makes us run.
He has a big red nose,
That nearly touches his toes.
He also plays hockey a lot,
He makes us hit the ball right on the dot.
He sometimes lets us fool about,
But I can tell you, he can *shout*.

Mrs BS is obviously Mr BS's wife,
So she is full of life.
She is going to be a mummy,
So she has got a very fat tummy.
She teaches us French,
While we sit on a bench.
We are learning about clothes,
And we have chausettes for our toes.
Mrs BS's French is cool,
Because she is no fool.

I don't think any of the BS's run this school,
Because they are too busy looking after the swimming pool.
After all the Headmaster runs it anyway,
Along with Mr Kay,
And all the other staff.
So the school is on the right path.
The teachers are cool,
That is why I like Wellow House School.

*Charlotte Huddlestone  (10)*
*Wellow House School*

## THE WIND IS IN MY FACE

The wind is in my face,
As I ride on my bike.
I am rushing down the long and winding road,
My pedals are turning and turning round,
Faster and faster I go,
Speeding down the road.
Riding and riding I go,
Rushing down the road.
Turning around the corner,
Dabbing on my brake,
Slower and slower I go,
Slower down the road,
Riding and riding I go,
Blowing down the road.
Pulling in the drive,
Skidding as I go,
Slower and slower I go,
Slower and slower I go.
Stopping in front of the drive,
Wheeling my bike into the garage.
Then to tea,
Just in time.

*Iain Hughes  (11)*
*Wellow House School*

# WHO RUNS THIS SCHOOL ANYWAY?

Mr Scully
Fixes things
Quick, get some pins
Got to fix some things
If it's big or small, ten feet tall
We will get the scaffolding from the sports hall
To get it into place
Quick, it's the alarm, fix it!
What is it this time?
Get some screws, got to
Fix some desks
Oh no, five days less
Of school, Mick thinks it is uncool
It must be him who runs this school.

*Oliver Robertshaw (9)*
*Wellow House School*